It's another Quality Book from CGP

This book is for anyone doing AQA Modular
GCSE Mathematics at Higher Level.

It contains lots of tricky questions designed
to make you sweat — because that's the only
way you'll get any better.

It's also got some daft bits in to try and make
the whole experience at least vaguely
entertaining for you.

What CGP is all about

Our sole aim here at CGP is to produce the highest quality
books — carefully written, immaculately presented and
dangerously close to being funny.

Then we work our socks off to get them
out to you — at the cheapest possible prices.

Contents

Unit 1 — Statistics and Number

Unit 2 — Number and Algebra

Unit 3 — Geometry and Algebra

Throughout the book, the more challenging questions are marked like this: Q1

Published by Coordination Group Publications Ltd.

Illustrated by Ruso Bradley, Lex Ward and Ashley Tyson

From original material by Richard Parsons.

Updated by:
Sarah Blackwood, Paul Jordin, Simon Little, Ali Palin, David Ryan,
Jane Towle and Dawn Wright.

Contributors:
Gill Allen
JE Dodds
Mark Haslam
C McLoughlin
John Waller
Janet West
Dave Williams

Proofreading:
Mark Moody and Julie Wakeling.

ISBN: 978 1 84762 492 5

Groovy website: www.cgpbooks.co.uk

Printed by Elanders Hindson Ltd, Newcastle upon Tyne.
Clipart sources: CorelDRAW® and VECTOR.

Text, design, layout and original illustrations © Richard Parsons 2010

Rounding Numbers

With all these rounding methods, you need to identify the last digit — e.g. if you're rounding 23.41 to 1 decimal place the last digit is 4. Then look at the next digit to the right. If it's 5 or more you round up, if it's 4 or less you round down.

Q1 Round these numbers to the required number of decimal places:

a) 62.1935 (1 dp)

b) 62.1935 (2 dp)

c) 62.1935 (3 dp)

d) 19.624328 (5 dp)

e) 6.2999 (3 dp)

f) π (3 dp)

Q2 Round these numbers to the required number of significant figures.

a) 1329.62 (3 SF)

b) 1329.62 (4 SF)

c) 1329.62 (5 SF)

d) 120 (1 SF)

e) 0.024687 (1 SF)

f) 0.024687 (4 SF)

Remember — the first significant figure is the first digit which isn't zero.

Q3 $K = 456.9873$
Write K correct to:

a) one decimal place

b) two decimal places

c) three decimal places

d) three significant figures

e) two significant figures

f) one significant figure.

Q4 Calculate the square root of 8. Write your answer to two decimal places.

Q5 Calculate, giving your answers to a sensible degree of accuracy:

a) $\dfrac{42.65 \times 0.9863}{24.6 \times 2.43}$

b) $\dfrac{13.63 + 7.22}{13.63 - 7.22}$

Rounding Numbers

Whenever a measurement is rounded off to a given unit, the <u>actual measurement</u> can be anything up to <u>half a unit bigger or smaller</u>.

1) <u>90 m</u> to the <u>nearest metre</u> could be anything between <u>85 m and 95 m</u>. (But not <u>exactly</u> equal to 95 m, or it would be rounded up to 100 m).

2) <u>700 people</u> to the nearest <u>10 people</u> could be anything between <u>695 people and 704 people</u>. (Because this only involves <u>whole</u> numbers.)

Q6 A bumper bag of icing sugar weighs 23.4 kg. What is this correct to the nearest kilogram?

Q7 David divides £15.20 by 3. What is the answer to the nearest penny?

Q8 The great racing driver Speedy Wheelman covered 234.65 miles during the course of one of his races. Give this distance correct to the nearest mile.

Q9 Jack's company pays his travel expenses.
They round the distance he drives to the nearest mile, and then pay 20p for every mile. In one week, Jack drives 95.45 miles. How much money can Jack claim back?

Q10 A pack of three model cars costs £14.30. John wants to work out what one model car would cost. What is the answer correct to the nearest penny?

Q11 Pru measured the length of her bedroom as 2.345 metres. Give this measurement correct to the nearest centimetre.

Q12 At a golf club, a putting green is given as being 5 m long to the nearest metre. Give the range of values that the actual length of the green could be.

Q13 Carlo weighs himself on some scales that are accurate to the nearest 10 g. The digital display shows his weight as 142.46 kg.
   a) What is the maximum that he could weigh?
   b) What is the minimum that he could weigh?

You need to add the errors for all the sides together.

Q14 a) The length of a rectangle is measured as 12 ± 0.1 cm. The width of the same rectangle is measured as 4 ± 0.1 cm. Calculate the perimeter of the rectangle, giving also the maximum possible error.
   b) A rectangle measures $A ± x$ cm in length and $B ± y$ cm in width. The formula $P = 2(A + B)$ is used to calculate the perimeter, P, of the rectangle. What is the maximum possible error in P?

Rounding and Accuracy

We're back to significant figures again. Still, it's all good practice, and practice makes...

1) For fairly CASUAL MEASUREMENTS, 2 SIGNIFICANT FIGURES are most appropriate.

Cooking — 250 g (2 SF) of sugar, not 253 g (3 SF) or 300 g (1 SF).

2) For IMPORTANT OR TECHNICAL THINGS, 3 SIGNIFICANT FIGURES are essential.

A length that will be cut to fit — you'd measure a shelf as 25.6 cm long, not 26 cm or 25.63 cm.

3) Only for REALLY SCIENTIFIC WORK would you need over 3 SIGNIFICANT FIGURES.

Only someone really keen would want to know the length of a piece of
string to the nearest tenth of a millimetre — like 34.46 cm, for example.

Q1 A field is roughly rectangular with a length of 33 m 48 cm and a width of
24 m 13 cm. Farmer Jim needs to calculate the area of the field so that he
knows how much fertiliser to buy. Calculate the area of the field in m² to:
a) 2 dp
b) 3 SF
c) State which of parts a) and b) would be the more reasonable value to use.

Just think casual, technical or really scientific...

Q2 Decide on an appropriate degree of accuracy for the following:
a) the total dry weight, 80872 kg, of the space shuttle OV-102
Columbia with its 3 main engines
b) the distance of 3.872 miles from Mel's house to Bryan's house
c) 1.563 m of fabric required to make a bedroom curtain
d) 152.016 kg of coal delivered to Jeff's house
e) 6 buses owned by the Partridge Flight Bus Company
f) the maximum night temperature of 11.721 °C forecast for
Birmingham by a TV weather presenter.

Q3 Round each of the following to an appropriate degree of accuracy:
a) 42.798 g of sugar used to make a cake
b) a hall carpet of length 7.216 m
c) 3.429 g of $C_6H_{12}O_6$ (sugar) for a scientific experiment
d) 1.132 litres of lemonade used in a fruit punch
e) 0.541 miles from Jeremy's house to the nearest shop
f) 28.362 miles per gallon.

Q4 Calculate, giving your answer to an
appropriate degree of accuracy:

a) $\dfrac{41.75 \times 0.9784}{22.3 \times 2.54}$

b) $\dfrac{12.54 + 7.33}{12.54 - 7.22}$

Calculation Bounds

To find the upper or lower bound of a calculation, you've just got to decide which version of the values involved (max or min) to use to get the biggest or smallest overall answer.

Q1 Jodie weighs herself on some scales that are accurate to the nearest 10 grams.
The digital display shows her weight as 64.78 kg.
a) What is the maximum that she could weigh?
b) What is the minimum that she could weigh?

Q2 A rectangular rug is 1.8 metres long and 0.7 metres wide.
Both measurements are given correct to one decimal place.

a) State the minimum possible length of the rug.
b) Calculate the maximum possible area of the rug.

Q3 Katherine is going on holiday and weighs her luggage to check
that it isn't over the weight allowance. She knows that her scales
weigh to the nearest 100 g. The scales read that her bag weighs
13.8 kg. What is the least that Katherine's bag could weigh?

Q4 Sandra has a parcel to post. To find out how much it will cost she weighs it.
a) A set of kitchen scales, that weigh to the nearest 10 g, show that the parcel weighs 90 g.
Write down the largest weight that the parcel could be.
b) Next she weighs the parcel on a different set of kitchen scales, which are accurate to the
nearest 5 g. The packet weighs 95 g. Write down the upper and lower bounds of the
weight of the package according to these scales.
c) The post office weighs the parcel on some electronic scales to the nearest gram.
It weighs 98 g. Can all the scales be right?

Q5 $R = \dfrac{S}{T}$ is a formula used by stockbrokers.
$S = 940$, correct to 2 significant figures and $T = 5.56$, correct to 3 significant figures.

a) For the value of S, write down the upper bound and the lower bound.
b) For the value of T, write down the upper bound and the lower bound.
c) Calculate the upper bound and lower bound for R.
d) Write down the value of R correct to an appropriate number of significant figures.

Remember — you don't always get the maximum value by using the biggest input values.

Calculation Bounds

Q6 $A = 13$, correct to 2 significant figures.
$B = 12.5$, correct to 3 significant figures.
   a) For the value of A, write down the upper bound and the lower bound.
   b) For the value of B, write down the upper bound and the lower bound.
   c) Calculate the upper bound and lower bound for C when $C = AB$.

Q7   Ash wants to put a new carpet in his living room. He has measured the floor as being 3.4 m × 5.2 m to the nearest 10 cm. What area of carpet should Ash buy to make sure he has enough to cover the whole floor?

Q8   Vince ran a 100 m race in 10.3 seconds. If the time was measured to the nearest 0.1 seconds and the distance to the nearest metre, what is the maximum value of his average speed, in metres per second?

Q9   A lorry travelled 125 kilometres in 1 hour and 50 minutes. If the time was measured to the nearest 10 minutes and the distance to the nearest five kilometres, what was the maximum value of the average speed of the lorry, in kilometres per hour?

Q10   Jimmy, Sarah and Douglas are comparing their best times for running the 1500 m.
Jimmy's best time is 5 minutes 30 seconds measured to the nearest 10 seconds.
Sarah's best time is also 5 minutes 30 seconds, but measured to the nearest 5 seconds.
Douglas' best time is 5 minutes 26 seconds measured to the nearest second.

   a) What are the upper and lower bounds for Sarah's best time?
   b) Of the three Douglas thinks that he is the quickest at running the 1500 m. Explain why this may not be the case.

UNIT 1 — STATISTICS AND NUMBER

Standard Index Form

Writing very big (or very small) numbers gets a bit messy with all those zeros if you don't use this standard index form. But of course, the main reason for knowing about standard form is... you guessed it — it's in the Exam.

Q1 Delilah is doing some calculations for her science homework.
She needs to give her answers as ordinary numbers.
How should she write the following answers?

a) 3.56×10
b) 3.56×10^3
c) 3.56×10^{-1}
d) 3.56×10^4

e) 0.082×10^2
f) 0.082×10^{-2}
g) 0.082×10
h) 0.082×10^{-1}

i) 157×10
j) 157×10^{-3}
k) 157×10^3
l) 157×10^{-1}

Q2 Write in standard form:

a) 2.56
b) 25.6
c) 0.256
d) 25 600

e) 95.2
f) 0.0952
g) 95 200
h) 0.000952

i) 4200
j) 0.0042
k) 42
l) 420.

Q3 Write in standard form:

a) 34.7×10
b) 73.004
c) 0.005×10^3
d) 9183×10^2

e) 15 million
f) 937.1×10^4
g) 0.000075
h) 0.05×10^{-2}

i) 534×10^{-2}
j) 621.03
k) 149×10^2
l) 0.003×10^{-4} .

When scientists write about massive things such as the universe, or tiny things such as cells and particles, it's often more convenient to write numbers in standard form. Write the numbers in Questions 4 to 7 in standard form.

Q4 The average diameter of a cell nucleus in a mammal is around 0.006 mm.

Q5 A billion = a thousand million   A trillion = a thousand billion.

Q6 A light year is 9 460 000 000 000 km (approx).

Q7 Nautilus covered 69 138 miles before having to refuel.

Q8 A tissue sample is three cells thick. Each cell has a thickness of 0.000004 m. What is the thickness of the tissue sample, in mm? Give your answer in standard form.

Q9 This table gives the diameter and distance from the Sun of some planets.

Planet	Distance from Sun (km)	Diameter (km)
Earth	1.5×10^8	1.3×10^4
Venus	1.085×10^8	1.2×10^4
Mars	2.28×10^8	6.8×10^3
Mercury	5.81×10^7	4.9×10^3
Jupiter	7.8×10^8	1.4×10^5
Neptune	4.52×10^9	4.9×10^4
Saturn	1.43×10^9	1.2×10^5

From the table write down which planet is:
a) smallest in diameter
b) largest in diameter
c) nearest to the Sun
d) furthest from the Sun.

Write down which planets are:
e) nearer to the Sun than the Earth
f) bigger in diameter than the Earth.

Standard Index Form

This stuff gets a lot easier if you know how to handle your calculator — read and learn.

Standard Index Form with a Calculator

Use the EXP button (or EE button) to enter numbers in standard index form.

Eg $1.7 \times 10^9 + 2.6 \times 10^{10}$. EXP +   . EXP =

The answer is 2.77^{10} which is read as 2.77×10^{10}

Q10 If $x = 4 \times 10^5$ and $y = 6 \times 10^4$ work out the value of
   a) xy **b)** $4x$ **c)** $3y$.

Q11 Which is <u>greater</u>, 4.62×10^{12} or 1.04×10^{13}, and <u>by how much</u>?

Q12 Which is <u>smaller</u> 3.2×10^{-8} or 1.3×10^{-9} and by how much?

Q13 The following numbers are <u>not</u> written in standard index form. Rewrite them correctly using standard index form.

   a) 42×10^6 **d)** 11.2×10^{-5} **g)** 17×10^{17}
   b) 38×10^{-5} **e)** 843×10^3 **h)** 28.3×10^{-5}
   c) 10×10^6 **f)** 42.32×10^{-4} **i)** 10×10^{-3}

Don't forget — when you're using a calculator, you've got to write the answer as 3.46×10^{27}, <u>not</u> as 3.46^{27}. If you do it the wrong way, it means something <u>completely</u> different.

Q14 What is <u>7 million</u> in standard index form?

Q15 The radius of the Earth is 6.38×10^3 km. What is the radius of the Earth measured in <u>cm</u>? Leave your answer in standard form.

Q16 One atomic mass unit is equivalent to 1.661×10^{-27} kg. What are <u>two</u> atomic mass units equivalent to (in standard index form)?

Q17 The length of a light year, the distance light can travel in one year, is 9.461×10^{15} m. How far can light travel in
   a) 2 years?
   b) 6 months?
   Write your answers in <u>standard form</u>.

Q18 a) The surface area of the Earth is approximately 5.1×10^8 km². Write this <u>without</u> using standard form.
   b) The area of the Earth covered by sea is 362 000 000 km². Write this in standard form.
   c) What is the approximate area of the Earth covered by land? Write your answer <u>without</u> using standard form.

Calculator Buttons

Q1 Using the x^2 button on your calculator, work out:

a) 1^2

b) 2^2

c) 11^2

d) 16^2

e) $(-1)^2$

f) 30^2

g) $(-5)^2$

h) 1000^2

i) 0^2

Q2 Using the $\sqrt{}$ button on your calculator, work out:

a) $\sqrt{16}$

b) $\sqrt{36}$

c) $\sqrt{289}$

d) $\sqrt{0}$

e) $\sqrt{3600}$

f) $\sqrt{400}$

g) $\sqrt{3}$

h) $\sqrt{7}$

i) $\sqrt{30}$

Q3 Use the $\sqrt[3]{}$ button on your calculator to work out:

a) $\sqrt[3]{1}$

b) $\sqrt[3]{0}$

c) $\sqrt[3]{343}$

d) $\sqrt[3]{1000}$

e) $\sqrt[3]{27}$

f) $\sqrt[3]{-27}$

g) $\sqrt[3]{-64}$

h) $\sqrt[3]{-5}$

Yeah, OK, we all know how to do sums on a calculator — but it can do so much more... check out the groovy powers button and the funky brackets buttons, not to mention the slinky memory button...

Q4 By calculating the bottom line (the denominator) first and storing it in your calculator, work out:

a) $\dfrac{21}{2 + \sin 30°}$

b) $\dfrac{\tan 15°}{12 + 12^2}$

c) $\dfrac{15}{\cos 30° + 22}$

d) $\dfrac{18}{3 + \sqrt[3]{12}}$

e) $\dfrac{12}{12 + \tan 60°}$

f) $\dfrac{18}{11 + \tan 77°}$

Calculator Buttons

Q5 Using [(--- and ---)] , calculate:

Here comes BODMAS...

a) $\dfrac{(14+18)}{(2\times 8)}$

c) $\dfrac{(9+(4\div 2))}{(11\times 3)}$

e) $\dfrac{12}{(8+9)(13-11)}$

b) $\dfrac{8}{(1\times 4)(8-6)}$

d) $\dfrac{14(4\times 8)}{(6+9)}$

f) $\dfrac{7(5+4)}{12(9\times 8)}$

Q6 Using the x^y or $\wedge$ button, find:

a) 2^0

d) π^2

g) $(\cos 30°)^5$

b) 4^{10}

e) 2^{-1}

h) 4.29^7

c) 2^{20}

f) 3^{10}

i) $(\sin 45°)^4$

Q7 Use your calculator to do the following calculations.
Write your answers in standard index form.

a) $4\times 10^3 + 5\times 10^2$

d) $9\times 10^5 \times 5\times 10^9$

b) $1\times 10^4 - 5\times 10^2$

e) $11.2\times 10^3 \times 16.7\times 10^2$

c) $6.2\times 10^5 + 7.3\times 10^4 + 5.1\times 10^6$

f) $(14\times 10^7 + 6\times 10^6) \times 8\times 10^2$

Q8 Work out the following. Write your answers as ordinary numbers.

a) $\dfrac{2\times 10^2}{5\times 10^1}$

d) $\dfrac{2.3\times 10^5}{4.6\times 10^6}$

b) $\dfrac{4.2\times 10^4}{2.1\times 10^5}$

e) $\dfrac{7.0\times 10^3}{3.5\times 10^5}$

c) $\dfrac{1.92\times 10^3}{9.6\times 10^2}$

f) $\dfrac{4.44\times 10^4}{1.11\times 10^2}$

Fractions With a Calculator

Fractions questions in Unit 1 should be a doddle when you have your trusty calculator...

Q1 The population of Australia is 18 million, of which 3.5 million people live in Sydney and 1 million people live in Perth.
a) What fraction of the population live in Perth?
b) What fraction of the population live in Perth or Sydney?

> This stuff is pretty easy — but you don't want to go making silly mistakes in the exam. Get the practice in now.

Q2 Green Island is split into six regions A, B, C, D, E and F. The areas of the six regions are 12, 2, 3, 18, 4, and 9 km² respectively.
a) What is the total area of the island?
b) What fraction of the island's area is taken up by the two largest regions?

Q3 In a consumer survey, 100 people stated their favourite vegetable. 25 people chose peas, 35 carrots and 32 runner beans.
a) How many of the 100 people chose a vegetable other than peas, carrots or runner beans?
b) What fraction of the 100 people chose carrots as their favourite vegetable?
c) What fraction of the 100 people chose peas as their favourite vegetable?
d) At least how many people chose a green vegetable as their favourite?
e) Not more than how many people chose a green vegetable as their favourite?

Q4 A ball is dropped from a height of 6 m.

6m

After each bounce the ball rises to 2/3 of its previous height. What height will it reach after the third bounce?

Q5 George wants to make a cake. The recipe requires 150 g each of flour, sugar and butter, and 3 eggs. George only has 2 eggs so he decides to make a smaller cake with the same proportions.
a) How much flour will George need to use?
b) If each egg weighs 25 g, how much will the cake weigh before it goes in the oven?
c) What fraction of the uncooked weight is flour?
d) If the cake loses 1/7 of its weight during baking (due to moisture loss) what will it weigh after baking?

Q6 Jenny goes shopping. She gets 1/3 off a bag priced £28, 1/5 off a dress priced £62 and 2/3 off a hat priced £14. How much money does she save?

Percentages

Make sure you can switch from fractions to decimals to percentages before you start.

Q1 Express each percentage as a decimal:

a) 20% **b)** 35% **c)** 2% **d)** 62.5%

Q2 Express each percentage as a fraction in its lowest terms:

a) 20% **b)** 3% **c)** 70% **d)** 84.2%

Q3 Express each of the following as a percentage:

a) $\frac{1}{8}$ **b)** 0.23 **c)** $\frac{12}{40}$ **d)** 0.34

Q4 In a French test, Lauren scored 17/20. What percentage is this?

Q5 87 out of 120 pupils at Backwater School have access to a computer. What percentage is this?

There are three types of percentage question. The first one is working out "something % of something else" — it's dead easy. Just remember to add it back on to the original amount if you've got a **VAT** question.

Q6 John bought a new TV. The tag in the shop said it cost £299 + VAT. If VAT is charged at 17½%, how much did he pay (to the nearest penny)?

Q7 Four friends stay at the Pickled Parrot Hotel for a night and each have an evening meal. Bed and Breakfast costs £37 per person and the evening meal costs £15 per person. How much is the total cost, if VAT is added at 17½%?

Q8 The owners of a museum are expecting a 14% increase in visitors next year. This year they had 20 200 visitors. How many visitors should they expect next year?

Percentages

Q9 Donald earns an annual wage of £23 500. He doesn't pay tax on the first £6400 that he earns. How much income tax does he pay a year if the rate of tax is:
   a) 25%
   b) 40%?

Q10 Tim is choosing between two cars to buy.
The first car is priced at £8495 and has 15% off.
The second car is priced at £8195 and has 12% off.
Which car is the cheapest? Show your working.

Q11 Tanya paid £6500 for her new car. Each year its value decreased by 8%.
   a) How much was it worth when it was one year old?
   b) How much was it worth when it was two years old?

Q12 Jeremy wanted a new sofa for his lounge. A local furniture shop had just what he was looking for — and for only £130.00 + VAT. Jeremy had £150 pounds in his bank account. If VAT was charged at 17½%, could Jeremy afford the sofa?

Here's the 2nd type — finding "something <u>as a percentage</u> of something else" — in this case you're looking at percentage <u>change</u>, so don't forget to find the difference in values first.

Q13 During a rainstorm, a water butt increased in weight from 10.4 kg to 13.6 kg.
What was the percentage increase (to the nearest percent)?

Q14 An electrical store reduces the price of a particular camera from £90.00 to £78.30.
What is the percentage reduction?

Q15 There are approximately 6000 fish and chip shops in the UK. On average, a fish and chip shop gets about 160 visitors each day. Given that the population of the UK is roughly 60 million, approximately what percentage of the population visit a fish and chip shop each day?

Q16 At birth, Veronica was 0.3 m tall. By adulthood she had grown to 1.5 m tall.
Calculate her height now as a percentage of her height at birth.

Percentages

Q17 Desmond's GCSE maths exam is next week. As part of his revision he attempted 31 questions on his least favourite topic of percentages. He got 21 questions fully right on the first attempt. Two days later he tried all 31 questions again and this time got 29 correct.
  a) What percentage of questions did he get correct on his first attempt?
  b) What percentage of questions did he get correct on his second attempt?
  c) What is the percentage improvement in Desmond's results?

Q18 I wish to invest £1000 for a period of three years and have decided to place my money with the Highrise Building Society on 1 January. If I choose to use the Gold Account I will withdraw the interest at the end of each year. If I choose to use the Silver Account I will leave the interest to be added to the capital at the end of each year.

Highrise Building Society

Gold Account   7.875% p.a
Silver Account   7.00% p.a

  a) Calculate the total interest I will receive if I use the Gold Account.
  b) Calculate the total interest I will receive if I use the Silver Account.
After some thought I decide to use the Gold Account and leave the interest to be added to the capital at the end of each year.
  c) Calculate the total interest I will now receive from the Gold Account.

Q19 If $L = MN$, what is the percentage increase in L if M increases by 15% and N increases by 20%?

Ooh... here's the 3ʳᵈ type — finding the <u>original value</u>. The bit most people get wrong is deciding whether the value given represents <u>more</u> or <u>less than 100%</u> of the original — so <u>always</u> check your answer <u>makes sense</u>.

Q20 In the new year sales Robin bought a tennis racket for £68.00. The original price had been reduced by 15%. What was the original price?

Q21 There are 360 people living in a certain village. The population of the village has grown by 20% over the past year.
  a) How many people lived in the village one year ago?
  b) If the village continues to grow at the same rate, how many whole years from today will it be before the population is more than twice its current size?

Compound Growth and Decay

Hey look — it's another of those "there is only one formula to learn and you use it for every question" topics.

So I reckon you'd better learn The Formula then...

Q1 A financial advisor is asked to predict the future value of his clients' investments. Calculate the amount in each of these accounts if:

a) £200 is invested for 10 years at 9% compound interest per annum

b) £500 is invested for 3 years at 7% compound interest per annum

c) £750 is invested for 30 months at 8% compound interest per annum

d) £1000 is invested for 15 months at 6.5% compound interest per annum.

Q2 A scientist is investigating a new strain of harmful bacteria. She needs to grow at least 4000 to have a big enough sample to run tests in the lab. The bacteria grows at the compound rate of 12% per hour, and she starts with 200 bacteria in the sample.

a) How many will there be after 3 hours?

b) How many will there be after 1 day?

c) After how many whole hours will there be at least 4000 bacteria?
(Solve this by trial and error.)

> Just make sure you get the _increase_ and _decrease_ the right way round... basically, just check your answer sounds like you'd expect — and if it doesn't, _do it again_.

Q3 An unknown radioactive element was discovered at the site of a suspected UFO crash. It was observed every day and the mass remaining was measured.
Initially there was 9 kg, but this decreased at the compound rate of 3% per day. How much radioactive element was left after:

a) 3 days

b) 6 days

c) 1 week

d) 4 weeks?
Give your answers to no more than 3 d.p.

Q4 Money is invested on the stock market. During a recession the value of the shares fall by 2% per week. Find the value of the stock if:

a) £2000 was invested for a fortnight

b) £30 000 was invested for four weeks

c) £500 was invested for 7 weeks

d) £100 000 was invested for a year.

Q5 Mrs Smith decides to invest £7000 in a savings account. She has the choice of putting all her money into an account paying 5% compound interest per annum or she can put half of her investment into an account paying 6% compound interest per annum and the remaining half into an account paying 4% per annum.
If she left the investment alone for 3 years, which is her best option and by how much?

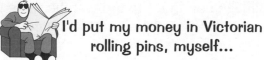

I'd put my money in Victorian rolling pins, myself...

Compound Growth and Decay

Q6 An antique vase has increased in value since its owner bought it five years ago at £220. If its value has appreciated by 16% per year, how much is it worth today?

Q7 A small clothing company is about to go bust as business has been slow. When the owner started up four years ago she bought machinery costing £3500. The depreciation on this machinery is typically 2½% per year. How much money could the owner raise by selling this machinery now, second-hand?

Q8 The activity of a radio-isotope decreases at a compound rate of 9% every hour. If the initial activity is recorded at 1100 counts per minute, what will it be after:
a) 2 hours
b) 4 hours
c) 1 day?
d) The activity of the same radio-isotope is recorded at just 66 counts per minute. Using trial and error, estimate the length of time elapsed since the recording of 1100 counts per minute.

Q9 A used car salesman is buying stock at an auction. Before the auction, he estimates the value of each car on offer using their original price, their age, and a depreciation of 14% each year. This value is the maximum amount he will bid for each car.
Calculate the maximum amount he should bid on these used cars:
a) a car which cost £8495 six months ago
b) a car which cost £34 000 eighteen months ago
c) a car which cost £13 495 two years ago
d) a car which cost £14 395 two years ago
e) a car which cost £11 295 three years ago
f) a car which cost £6 795 twelve months ago.

Q10 Property prices in one area have depreciated in value by 5% per year over the last three years. Calculate the expected value today of these properties, to the nearest pound:
a) a house bought for £150 000, 3 years ago
b) a bungalow bought for £115 000, 2 years ago
c) a flat bought for £80 000, six months ago
d) a factory bought for £500 000, 1 year ago.

Q11 A culture of bacteria increases in number at a compound rate of 0.4% per hour. If initially there was a culture of 50 cells, how many cells will there be after:
a) 3 hours
b) 8 hours 30 minutes
c) 135 mins
d) 2 days?

Q12 The population of a country is 16 million, and the annual compound growth rate is estimated to be 1.3%. Predict the country's population in:
a) 4 years' time
b) 20 years' time.

Ratios

I don't want to spoil the surprise, but you're going to need your calculator for this bit — get your finger on that fraction button...

RATIOS are like FRACTIONS which are like DECIMALS

We can treat the RATIO 3:4 like the FRACTION ¾, which is 0.75 as a DECIMAL.

Watch out though — this isn't ¾ of the total:
If there are girls and boys in the ratio **3:4**, it means there's ¾ as many girls as boys.
So if there's **8 boys**, there's **¾ × 8 = 6 girls**.

Q1 Write these ratios in their simplest forms:
  a) 6:8   **c)** 1.5:3   **e)** 2 weeks:4 days
  b) 5:20   **d)** 2¼:4   **f)** £1.26:14p

Q2 A rectangle has sides in the ratio 1:2. Calculate the length of the longer side if the shorter side is:
  a) 3 cm   **b)** 5.5 cm   **c)** 15.2 m

Calculate the length of the shorter side if the longer side is:
  d) 3 cm   **e)** 5.5 cm   **f)** 15.2 m

Q3 Oak and ash saplings are planted along a roadside in the ratio 2:3 respectively. If there are 20 oak saplings, how many ash saplings are there?

Q4 The recipe for flapjacks is 250 g of oats, 150 g of brown sugar and 100 g of margarine. What fraction of the mixture is:
  a) oats?
  b) sugar?

Q5 An architect is drawing the plan of a house to a scale of 1 cm to 3 m.
  a) Write this ratio in its simplest form.
  b) How wide is a room that appears as 2 cm on the drawing?
  c) The hall is 10 m long. How long will the architect need to make it on the drawing?

Make sure you convert to the same units when you're working out the ratio.

Q6 The ratio of girls to boys in a school is 7:6. If there are 245 girls in the school, how many
  a) boys are there?
  b) pupils are there in total?

Q7

I picked some strawberries after a few wet days. Some were nibbled by snails, some were mouldy and some fine. The ratio was 2:3:10 respectively. If <u>9 strawberries were mouldy</u> how many:
  a) were fine?
  b) were not fine?
  c) What fraction of the total amount were fine?

Collecting Data

Data can be qualitative or quantitative, discrete or continuous — know the differences.

Q1 **a)** Write down a definition of secondary data.
 b) What is the name given to data which you collect yourself?

Q2 Say whether each of these data collection methods gives primary or secondary data.
 a) Using data from the 1901 national census.
 b) Doing an experiment to see how long students take to complete a puzzle.
 c) Using temperature charts from a national newspaper.

Q3 Zac collects some data about his school. The data items are listed below.
 Say whether each data item is qualitative or quantitative.

 a) The colours of pants worn by the teachers.
 b) The number of students late to school from each form on the first day of term.
 c) The distance travelled to school by each student.
 d) The star sign of each student.

Q4 Amy collects some data at her school sports day. The data items are listed below.
 Say whether each data item is discrete or continuous.
 a) The number of competitors in each event.
 b) The finishing times of each competitor in the 100-metre sprint.
 c) The total number of points scored by each form at the end of the day.
 d) The distances jumped by each competitor in the long jump.

Q5 The local council wants to investigate whether or not road traffic accidents
 at a certain junction are more likely to occur during the morning rush hour
 (between 8 a.m and 9 a.m.) than any other time of day.

 What data does the local council need to collect?

 **If you're doing stats it's easy to have loads and loads
 of data, which can make it pretty hard to analyse.
 So it helps to group it together so it's more manageable.**

Q6 Fred asked each of his 30 classmates how long (in minutes) it took
 them to eat their dinner. Here are the results he recorded:

```
42 13 3   31 15 20 19 1   59 14
8   25 16 27 4   55 32 31 31 10
32 17 16 19 29 42 43 30 29 18
```

 a) Group the data appropriately
 and fill in the table.
 b) State one disadvantage
 of grouping data.

Length of time (mins)					
Number of people					

Collecting Data

Questionnaires are a great way to gather information. But you need to think carefully about how you design, distribute and collect them so you get the information you want.

Q7 Stanley is researching the use of the school canteen.
He asks this question to a sample of students at the school:
How often do you use the canteen? Tick one of the boxes.

Very often ☐   *Quite often* ☐

Not very often ☐   *Never* ☐

a) Give one criticism of Stanley's question.
b) Write a question that Stanley could use to find out how often students at his school use the canteen.

Q8 A drinks company is trying to profile their customers. They want to find out which age groups to target their marketing at. They use this question as part of a questionnaire:
How old are you?
i) Under 18   ii) 18 to 30   iii) 30 to 40   iv) 40 to 60   v)   over 60
a) Give one criticism of this question.
b) How would you improve this question?

Q9 Decide if each of the following questions are suitable for a survey to find which of five desserts (cheesecake, fruit salad, sherry trifle, knickerbocker glory and chocolate cake) people like the most. Give a reason for each of your answers.
a) Do you like cheesecake, fruit salad, sherry trifle, knickerbocker glory or chocolate cake?
b) How often do you eat dessert?
c) Which is your favourite out of: cheesecake; fruit salad; sherry trifle; knickerbocker glory; chocolate cake?
d) What is your favourite dessert?
e) Is your favourite dessert: cheesecake; fruit salad; sherry trifle; knickerbocker glory; chocolate cake; none of these?

Q10 Pauline is the manager of a small café. She knows that some of her customers buy cold drinks from the cold drinks machine, some buy hot drinks from the hot drinks machine and some people buy snacks and drinks at the counter.
Pauline would like to use a questionnaire to find out whether she should stock a new brand of cola. Here is part of Pauline's questionnaire:

Café Questionnaire

1) **Please tick the box to show how often you visit the cafe:**

daily ☐   weekly ☐   fortnightly ☐   monthly ☐   less than monthly ☐

a) Using the same style, design another question that Pauline can include in her questionnaire.
b) Pauline hands out her questionnaire as she serves customers at the counter.
Give a reason why this is a suitable or unsuitable way to hand out the questionnaire.

Sampling

**When you're collecting data, getting the sample right is essential
so that your results are <u>representative</u> of the population.**

Q1 Professor Xavier Entric is doing a research project on
the lifespan of moorland dung beetles in the UK.

a) What population would Professor Entric use for his research?

b) Give one reason why Professor Entric would use a sample,
rather than surveying the whole population.

Q2 Fred is doing a statistical project on the distances travelled by students to his school.
The table below gives a breakdown of the numbers
of students in each year group at Fred's school.

Don't forget that the proportion of any group in a sample has to be the same as the proportion in the population.

Year Group	7	8	9	10	11
Number of Students	398	405	401	197	199

Fred decides to use a stratified random sample with 40 students.

a) Give a reason why Fred has decided to choose a stratified sample.

b) How many Year 7 students would be in the sample?

c) In another stratified random sample from the same school, there are ten Year 11 students.
How many students are in the sample altogether?

Q3 A newspaper contained the following article regarding the amount of exercise teenagers
take outside school.

a) Suggest 3 questions that you could use
in a survey to find out whether this is
true at your school.

b) At a particular school there are 300
pupils in each of years 7 to 11. There
are approximately equal numbers of
girls and boys.
Describe how you would select 10%
of the pupils for a stratified sample
which is representative of all the
pupils at the school.

Over half of all teenagers do no exercise at all. Only one in ten play team sports or take part in individual sports.
blah-blah-blah-blah-blah
blah-blah-blah-blah-blah
blah-blah-blah-blah-blah
blah-blah-blah-blah-blah
blah-blah-blah-blah-blah
blah-blah-blah-blah-blah
blah-blah-blah-blah-blah
blah-blah-blah-blah-blah
blah-blah-blah-blah-blah
blah-blah-blah-blah-blah
blah-blah-blah-blah-blah

Q4 Give a reason why the following methods of sampling are poor:

a) a survey carried out inside a newsagents concluded that 80% of the population buy a
daily newspaper

b) a phone poll conducted at 11 am on a Sunday morning revealed that less than 2% of the
population regularly go to church

c) 60% of the population were estimated to watch the 9 o'clock news each evening after a
survey was carried out at a bridge club.

Mean, Median, Mode and Range

For finding the **mode** and **median** put the data in order of size — it's much easier to find the most frequent and middle values.

The **mean** involves a bit more calculation, but hey, you're doing maths...

Q1 The local rugby team scored the following number of tries in their first 10 matches of the season:

3	5	4	2	0	1	3	0	3	4

Find their modal number of tries.

Q2 Find the mean, median, mode and range of these numbers:

1	2	–2	0	1	8	3	–3	2	4	–2	2

Q3 A company has 9 employees in the sales department who earn commission. They are advertising for another salesperson and want to say in the advert how much commission their staff earn on average. The amount of commission the 9 existing salespeople earned last year is as follows:

£13,000	£9,000	£7,500
£18,000	£12,000	£7,500
£23,000	£15,000	£11,500

a) Find the mean, median and mode of their earnings.

b) Which one does not give a good indication of their average commission?

c) Which should the company put in the advert, and why?

Q4 Molly is writing a letter of complaint to the bus company because she thinks her bus to school is regularly late. Over 3 weeks, Molly kept a record of how many minutes her bus was either early or late, and put this in her letter. (She used + for late and – for early.)

+2	–1	0	+5	–4
–7	0	–8	0	+4
–4	–3	+14	+2	0

a) Calculate the mean lateness/earliness of the bus.

b) Calculate the median.

c) What is the mode?

d) The bus company use the answers to **a)**, **b)** and **c)** to claim they are always on time. Is this true?

Careful with this — you have to use the averages to find the total weight, then divide to find the new average.

Q5 The average weight of the 11 players in a football team was 72.5 kg. The average weight of the 5 reserve players was 75.6 kg. What was the average weight of the whole squad? (Give your answer to 3 s.f.)

Q6 The mean daily weight of potatoes sold in a greengrocer's from Monday to Friday was 14 kg. The mean daily weight of potatoes sold from Monday to Saturday was 15 kg. How many kg of potatoes were sold on Saturday?

UNIT 1 — STATISTICS AND NUMBER

Mean, Median, Mode and Range

Q7 Colin averaged 83% over 3 exams. His average for the first two exams was 76%. What was Colin's score in the final exam?

Q8 The range for a certain list of numbers is 26, one of the numbers in the list is 48.
  a) What is the lowest possible value a number in the list could be?
  b) What is the highest possible value that could be in the list?

Q9 An ordinary dice is rolled 6 times, landing on a different number each time.
  a) What is the mean score?
  b) What is the median score?
  c) What is the range of scores?

Q10 The bar graph shows the amount of time Jim and Bob spend watching TV during the week.

  a) Find the mean amount of time per day each spends watching TV.

  b) Find the range of times for each of them.

  c) Using your answers from **a)** and **b)**, comment on what you notice about the way they watch TV.

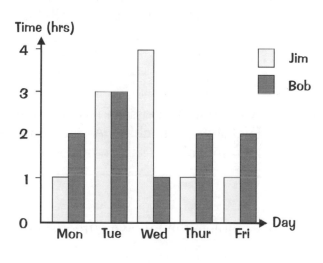

Q11 Mr Jones posted 88 Christmas cards first class on Monday. His friends received them over the week: 40 on Tuesday, 28 on Wednesday, 9 on Thursday, 6 on Friday and the remainder on Saturday.
  a) Find the modal number of days it took for the cards to arrive.
  b) Find the median number of days it took for the cards to arrive.
  c) "The majority of first class post arrives within 2 days." Is the above statement true or false in the light of the data?

Q12 In each of the following cases, decide which average is referred to:
  a) this average is least appropriate when the total number of values is small
  b) this average is least affected if one of the values is removed at random
  c) this average is most affected by the presence of extreme values.

Frequency Tables

You've got to be able to do these in both row and
column form, because they could give you either one.
There's no real difference, and the rules are still the same.

Q1 To monitor their annual performance, a travel company logs all calls to their sales desk.
The number of calls per day received by the sales desk over a given year are shown here.

No. of Calls	10	11	12	13	14	15	16 and over
No. of Days	110	70	120	27	18	12	8

a) Find the median number of calls.
b) Find the modal number of calls.

Q2 A student has classes in Mathematics (M),
English (E), French (F), Art (A) and Science (S).
Her timetable is shown opposite.

Monday	S S E E A
Tuesday	E M M A A
Wednesday	S M E F F
Thursday	F E E A S
Friday	M M E S S

a) Complete the following frequency table for a week's lessons:

b) Calculate the number of French
lessons that the student will attend
during a 12-week term.

Subject	M	E	F	A	S
Frequency					

c) What is the modal lesson?

Q3 20 pupils are asked to estimate the length (to the nearest m) of their gardens.
Here are the results: 10, 8, 6, 4, 10, 8, 0, 14, 12, 8, 10, 6, 1, 6, 10, 8, 6, 6, 8, 8
Copy the frequency table below and put the estimates in.

a) Find the mode of the data.
b) Find the median of the data.
c) State the range of the data.

Length (m)	4 and under	6	8	10	12	14 and over
Frequency						

Frequency Tables

Q4 130 female bus drivers were weighed to the nearest kg.

a) Find the median weight
b) Find the modal weight
c) Calculate the mean weight by first completing the table.

Weight (kg)	Frequency	Weight × Frequency
51	40	
52	30	
53	45	
54	10	
55	5	

Q5 A football magazine rates teams according to how many goals they're likely to score in a match, based on their last 20 matches. The table below shows the number of goals scored by Spark Bridge Wanderers over this period.

No. of goals	0	1	2	3	4	5	6
Frequency	1	1	1	8	3	4	2

Find the mean, mode, upper quartile, lower quartile and median of the data.

Q6 A tornado has struck the hamlet of Moose-on-the-Wold. Many houses have had windows broken. The frequency table shows the devastating effects.

No. of windows broken per house	0	1	2	3	4	5	6
Frequency	5	3	4	11	13	7	2

a) Find the modal number of broken windows.
b) Find the median number of broken windows.
c) Calculate the mean number of broken windows

Q7 Using the computerised till in a shoe shop, the manager can predict what stock to order from the previous week's sales.
Opposite is the tabulated printout for last week for men's shoes.

Shoe size	5	6	7	8	9	10	11
frequency	9	28	56	70	56	28	9

a) The mean, mode and median for this data can be compared. For each of the following statements decide whether it is true or false.
  i)   The <u>mode</u> for this data is <u>70</u>.
  ii) The <u>mean</u> is <u>greater than</u> the <u>median</u> for this distribution.
  iii) The mean, median and mode are <u>all equal</u> in this distribution.

b) What <u>percentage</u> of customers bought shoes of the <u>mean size</u> from last week's sales data:

  i) 30% **ii)** 70% **iii)** 0.273% or **iv)** 27.3%?

Grouped Frequency Tables

Q1   The speeds of 32 skiers at a certain corner of a downhill course are tabulated below.

Speed (km/h)	$40 \leq s < 45$	$45 \leq s < 50$	$50 \leq s < 55$	$55 \leq s < 60$	$60 \leq s < 65$
Frequency	4	8	10	7	3
Mid-Interval					
Frequency × Mid-Interval					

a) By completing the frequency table, estimate the mean speed.
b) How many skiers were travelling at less than 55 km/h?
c) How many skiers were travelling at 50 km/h or faster?

Q2   The weights in kg of 18 newly felled trees are noted below:
272.7   333.2   251.0   246.5   328.0   259.6   200.2   312.8   344.3
226.8   362.0   348.3   256.1   232.9   309.7   398.0   284.5   327.4

a) Complete the frequency table.

Weight (kg)	Tally	Frequency	Mid-Interval	Frequency × Mid-Interval
$200 \leq w < 250$				
$250 \leq w < 300$				
$300 \leq w < 350$				
$350 \leq w < 400$				

b) Estimate the mean weight using the frequency table.
c) What is the modal group?

Q3   48 numbers are recorded below:

0.057   0.805   0.056   0.979   0.419   0.160   0.534   0.763
0.642   0.569   0.773   0.055   0.349   0.892   0.664   0.136
0.528   0.792   0.085   0.546   0.549   0.908   0.639   0.000
0.614   0.478   0.421   0.472   0.292   0.579   0.542   0.356
0.070   0.890   0.883   0.333   0.033   0.323   0.544   0.668
0.094   0.049   0.049   0.999   0.632   0.700   0.983   0.356

a) Transfer the data into the frequency table.

Number	$0 \leq n < 0.2$	$0.2 \leq n < 0.4$	$0.4 \leq n < 0.6$	$0.6 \leq n < 0.8$	$0.8 \leq n < 1$
Tally					
Frequency					
Mid-Interval					
Frequency × Mid-Interval					

b) Write down the modal class(es).
c) Which group contains the median?
d) Estimate the mean value.

Cumulative Frequency

Q1 Using the cumulative frequency curve, read off the:
  a) median
  b) lower quartile
  c) upper quartile
  d) interquartile range.

Q2 The following box plot shows the ages in years of trees in a wood.

Age in years

  a) What is the median age of the trees?
  b) What is the upper quartile value?
  c) What is the interquartile range?

Q3 The number of passengers using a bus service each day has been recorded over a 4-week period. The data is presented in the table below:

No. passengers	$0 \leq n < 50$	$50 \leq n < 100$	$100 \leq n < 150$	$150 \leq n < 200$	$200 \leq n < 250$	$250 \leq n < 300$
Frequency	2	7	10	5	3	1
Cumulative Frequency						
Mid-Interval						
Frequency × Mid-Interval						

A mean passenger

  a) By completing the table, estimate the mean number of passengers.
  b) By plotting a cumulative frequency curve, determine the median value.
  c) What is the modal group?

> With cumulative frequency you always plot the highest value from each class.

Q4 40 pupils have taken an exam and their marks are recorded in a frequency table.

Mark (%)	$0 \leq m < 20$	$20 \leq m < 40$	$40 \leq m < 60$	$60 \leq m < 80$	$80 \leq m < 100$
Frequency	2	12	18	5	3
Cumulative Frequency					

  a) Complete the table and plot the cumulative frequency curve.
  b) What is the value of the lower quartile?
  c) What is the interquartile range?
  d) What is the median mark?

Cumulative Frequency

Q5 One hundred scores for a board game are presented in the table below.

Score	$31 \leq s < 41$	$41 \leq s < 51$	$51 \leq s < 61$	$61 \leq s < 71$	$71 \leq s < 81$	$81 \leq s < 91$	$91 \leq s < 101$
Frequency	4	12	21	32	19	8	4
Cumulative Frequency							

a) What is the modal group?
b) Which group contains the median score?
c) By plotting the cumulative frequency curve determine the actual value of the median score.
d) Find the interquartile range.

Q6 The following frequency table gives the distribution of the lives of electric bulbs.

a) Complete the frequency table.

Life (hours)	Frequency	Cumulative Frequency
$900 \leq L < 1000$	10	
$1000 \leq L < 1100$	12	
$1100 \leq L < 1200$	15	
$1200 \leq L < 1300$	18	
$1300 \leq L < 1400$	22	
$1400 \leq L < 1500$	17	
$1500 \leq L < 1600$	14	
$1600 \leq L < 1700$	9	

b) Which group contains the median value?
c) By drawing the cumulative frequency curve, find the actual value of the median.
d) Determine values for the upper and lower quartiles.

Q7 30 pupils recorded the time taken (minutes : seconds) to boil some water.
Here are their results:

2:37 2:37 3:17 3:30 2:45 2:13 3:18 3:12 3:38 3:29
3:04 3:24 4:13 3:01 3:11 2:33 3:37 4:24 3:59 3:11
3:22 3:13 2:57 3:12 3:07 4:17 3:31 3:42 3:51 3:24

a) By using a tally, transfer the data into the frequency table.
b) Draw the cumulative frequency curve.

Time	$2:00 \leq t < 2:30$	$2:30 \leq t < 3:00$	$3:00 \leq t < 3:30$	$3:30 \leq t < 4:00$	$4:00 \leq t < 4:30$
Tally					
Frequency					
Cumulative Frequency					

c) Using your graph, read off the median and the upper and lower quartiles.
d) What is the interquartile range?

UNIT 1 — STATISTICS AND NUMBER

Histograms and Dispersion

It's the <u>size that counts</u>... You've got to look at the <u>area</u> of the bars to find the frequency. That means looking at the <u>width</u> as well as the height.

Q1 The Bog Snorkelling Appreciation Society conducts a survey on the ages of all their members. The histogram below shows the age distribution of the people surveyed. The Society organises a 'Seniors' bog snorkelling event for members aged 60 or older. Use the graph to estimate the maximum number of people that might take part.

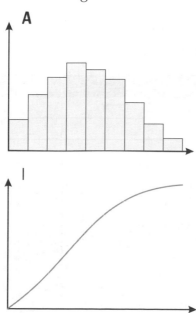

Use the key to work out the frequencies.

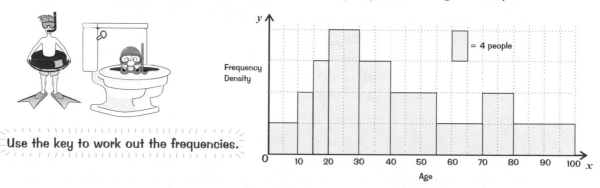

Q2 The weight of honey collected from several beehives is tabulated below.
  a) Complete the frequency table by calculating the frequency densities.
  b) Draw a histogram to represent this data.
  c) Use your histogram to estimate the number of beehives that produced more than 6 kg of honey.

Weight (kg)	$0 \le w < 2$	$2 \le w < 4$	$4 \le w < 7$	$7 \le w < 9$	$9 \le w < 15$
Frequency	3	2	6	9	12
Frequency density					

Q3 Match the histograms to their corresponding cumulative frequency curves.

Histograms and Dispersion

 Know your shapes — they're bound to ask you what different-shaped graphs mean, so get learning.

Q4 A group of sixth formers took part in a survey to see how much time they spent watching TV each week.

a) Complete the table by filling in the frequency density column.

b) How many students took part in the survey?

c) Represent the data as a histogram.

d) Estimate the number of students that watch more than 7, but less than 13 hours each week.

No. of hours	Frequency	Frequency density
$0 \leq h < 1$	6	
$1 \leq h < 3$	13	
$3 \leq h < 5$	15	
$5 \leq h < 8$	9	
$8 \leq h < 10$	23	
$10 \leq h < 15$	25	
$15 \leq h < 20$	12	

Q5 Below are two histograms — one shows the weights of a sample of 16 year olds, and the other shows the weights of a sample of 1 kg bags of sugar. Say which is which.

Q6 A local newspaper employee has collected data on the salaries of 100 people living in the area. His data is shown in the table below.

Salary (£1000s)	$0 \leq s < 10$	$10 \leq s < 20$	$20 \leq s < 30$	$30 \leq s < 40$	$40 \leq s < 50$
Frequency	10	25	42	20	3
Frequency Density					

a) Complete the table and draw a histogram to show the data.

b) The newspaper prints this histogram alongside the one shown on the right. It represents data from an identical survey done 10 years earlier. Write a comment comparing current salaries and those from 10 years ago.

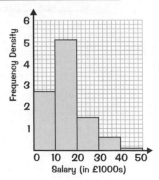

Histograms and Dispersion

Q7   A farmer keeps track of the amount of milk produced by his cows each day.

Amount of Milk (Litres)	Frequency	Frequency Density	Mid-Interval	Frequency × Mid-Interval
$0 \leqslant C < 1$	6			
$1 \leqslant C < 5$	6			
$5 \leqslant C < 8$	6			
$8 \leqslant C < 10$	6			
$10 \leqslant C < 15$	6			
$15 \leqslant C < 20$	6			

a) Complete the frequency table.
b) Use the mid-interval technique to estimate the mean.
c) Draw a histogram to show the data.
d) On how many days is less than 8 litres produced?

Q8   The publishers of a teen magazine want to increase its price.
To help them choose the best price, they carried out a survey of
188 readers to see how much pocket money they receive each week.

Amount (£)	Frequency	Frequency Density	Mid-Interval	Frequency × Mid-Interval
$0 \leq A < 0.50$	11			
$0.50 \leq A < 1.00$	25			
$1.00 \leq A < 1.30$	9			
$1.30 \leq A < 1.50$	12			
$1.50 \leq A < 1.80$	24			
$1.80 \leq A < 2.50$	21			
$2.50 \leq A < 3.10$	54			
$3.10 \leq A < 4.10$	32			

a) By first completing the table, estimate the mean amount of pocket money.
b) What is the modal class?

    The publishers decide that £1.40 would be a reasonable price, but they want to check that at least 75% of readers could afford to buy the magazine with their pocket money.

c) Draw a histogram of the data and estimate how many readers receive less than £1.40.
d) Do 75% of readers receive £1.40 or more?

Scatter Graphs

A <u>SCATTER GRAPH</u> is just a load of points on a graph that <u>end up in a bit of a mess</u>, rather than in a nice line or curve. There's a fancy word to say how much of a mess they're in — it's <u>CORRELATION</u>.

Q1 Match the following diagrams with the most appropriate descriptive label.

Labels: (P) Strong positive correlation   (S) Moderate negative correlation
       (Q) Exact negative correlation   (T) Medium correlation
       (R) Little or no correlation   (U) Exact positive correlation.

Q2 Adam thinks that cricketers who are good at batting must also be good at bowling. The bowling and batting averages for the members of his local team are given in the table.

Batting	8	13	17	26	29	35	37	40	45	52	57
Bowling	32	13	22	31	14	22	6	10	50	39	12

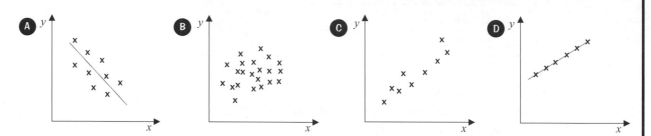

Good batters have a <u>high</u> batting average.
Good bowlers have a <u>low</u> bowling average.

a) Draw a scatter diagram for the above data.
b) State the type of correlation, if any.
c) Is Adam correct in his assumption? Explain your answer.

Q3 The examination results (%) for a class of students for 2 exams are shown in the table.

Physics	97	61	36	56	48	84	83	79	26	66
Chemistry	98	65	49	66	60	88	87	85	43	78

a) Represent the data with a scatter graph.
b) State the type of correlation, if any.
c) The students' science teacher thinks that the better a student is at physics, the better they'll be at chemistry. Do the exam results support this view?

Scatter Graphs

Q4   8 friends are comparing heights and shoe sizes to see if they are correlated. The data is tabulated below:

Height	4'6"	4'8"	5'2"	5'5"	5'8"	5'10"	6'	6'6"
Shoe size	4	5	4.5	5	6	8	9	12

a) Plot the points on a scatter graph.
b) Are the points positively or negatively correlated?
c) Write a statement to describe the link between height and shoe size, from this data.
d) By fitting an appropriate line, estimate the shoe size of another friend who is 6'2".

Q5   10 people took 2 exams in Welding for Beginners. The table shows the marks obtained.

Candidate	1	2	3	4	5	6	7	8	9	10
Exam 1 (%)	85	30	55	10	40	20	0	95	65	40
Exam 2 (%)	70	25	50	15	70	25	5	80	60	35

a) Draw a scatter graph representing this information.
b) Draw a line of best fit.
c) One of the candidates revised much more for the second exam than the first. Which candidate do you think this was?
d) Clive only sat the first exam, obtaining a mark of 50%. Use your scatter graph to estimate the mark that he might have achieved if he had sat the second exam.

Q6   Janine is convinced that the more expensive cookery books contain more pages. To test out her theory, she has compiled this table:

Price	£4.25	£5.00	£4.75	£6.25	£7.50	£8.25	£4.75	£5.00	£6.75	£3.25	£3.75
No. of pages	172	202	118	184	278	328	158	138	268	84	98

a) Draw a scatter graph to represent this information.
b) Draw in a line of best fit.
c) Use your line to estimate the price of a book containing 250 pages.

Q7   A local electrical store has kept a log of the number of CD players sold at each price:

Price (£)	£80	£150	£230	£310	£380	£460
No. Sold	27	24	22	19	17	15

a) Draw this information as a scatter graph, using suitable axes.
b) Draw a line of best fit and use it to estimate:
   i) the number of CD players the shopkeeper could expect to sell for £280
   ii) how much the shopkeeper should charge if he wanted to sell exactly 25 CD players.
c) Is the data positively or negatively correlated?

Stem and Leaf Diagrams

The key to success with stem and leaf diagrams is, well, the key really.
Remember to include one if you're drawing your own diagram.

Q1 List the values shown in this stem and leaf diagram in
ascending order.

Just to start you off, the first five values are:
3, 3, 3, 5, 8...

0	3 3 3 5 8 8 9
1	2 3 4 4 8 8 9
2	0 2 2 4
3	1 3

Key: 1 | 4   means 14

Q2 This stem and leaf diagram shows the marks in a test for a group of 25 students.

0	
5	0 1
10	0 1 4
15	0 2 2 3 3 4
20	1 1 1 2 4 4
25	1 2 3 4
30	1 4 4
35	4

Key: 15 | 3 means 18

Use the information in the diagram to answer these questions:
a) Find the number of students scoring 18.
b) Find the number of students scoring 10-15 inclusive.
c) Find the number of students scoring 28 or more:
d) Find the highest score.
e) Find the range of the scores.
f) Find the modal score.
g) Find the mean score.
h) Find the median score.

If you've got class-widths of 5,
you ADD the numbers TOGETHER.

Q3 I did a survey to find out how many living relatives my friends have.
Here are my results:

37 23 48 21 33 39
8 31 11 41 50 7
22 18 15 26 29 13

Draw a stem and leaf diagram to represent this data.
Use this key:

Key: 1 | 4   means 14

Q4 Use the information from this line graph to create your own stem and leaf diagram,
using class-widths of 5. Then make a key
to show how to use your diagram.

40	
35	
30	
25	
20	

Key: | means

Weight of 8 year olds (in kg)

Pie Charts

Everyone loves a pie chart. Oh, no, sorry, that's pies...

When constructing a pie chart, follow the three steps:

1) Add up the numbers in each sector to get the <u>TOTAL</u>.
2) Divide 360° by the <u>TOTAL</u> to get the <u>MULTIPLIER</u>.
3) Multiply <u>EVERY</u> number by the <u>MULTIPLIER</u> to get the <u>ANGLE</u> of each <u>SECTOR</u>.

Q1 A company that makes and sells pies wants to add a nutritional information diagram to their packaging. <u>Construct a pie chart</u> using the template on the right, to show the following nutritional data for one of their pies:

Contents of Pie	Amount per 100 g
Carbohydrate	35 g
Protein	15 g
Fat	10 g
Magical fairy dust	40 g

Q2 According to the tourist board for the Hindle Isles, 380,000 people visited the biggest island in the group, Sherrington, in 2009. The <u>distribution</u> of tourists for the <u>whole group of islands</u> is shown in the pie chart. Use a <u>protractor</u> on the diagram to find the number of tourists visiting the other islands in 2009 (rounded to the nearest 10,000).

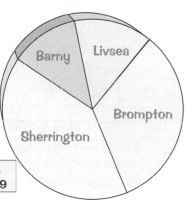

> Use the info you're given to find the number of tourists represented by 1°.

The distribution of visitors to the Hindle Isles in 2009

Q3 The pie chart shows the results of a survey of forty 11 year olds when asked what their <u>favourite vegetable</u> is with Sunday lunch. Which one of the following may be <u>deduced</u> from the information in the <u>pie chart</u>?

a) Potatoes are the <u>least popular</u> vegetable.
b) 3/4 of the children <u>like potatoes</u> of some type.
c) 1/10 of the children like <u>carrots or cauliflower</u>.
d) 11/40 of the children asked what their favourite vegetable is, replied "<u>Don't eat vegetables</u>."

Q4 The pie charts opposite appear in a newspaper article about a local election. Nicki says that more people voted for the Green party in 2009 than in 2005.

Comment on <u>whether it's possible</u> to tell this from the pie charts.

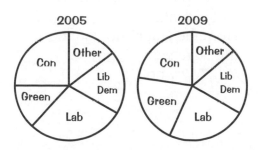

UNIT 1 — STATISTICS AND NUMBER

Graphs and Charts

Q1 A sprinter is training for an athletics event. He has recorded the times of some of his training runs in the frequency table below.

Time (s)	$9 \leq t < 10$	$10 \leq t < 11$	$11 \leq t < 12$	$12 \leq t < 13$
Frequency	6	9	4	3

a) Display this information as a frequency polygon.
b) How many training runs has the sprinter recorded?
c) How many of his runs were quicker than 12 seconds?

Q2 The grading for skiers to be awarded certificates is as follows:
B - beginner, I - intermediate, G - good, VG - very good, R - racer.

To clarify the situation for a school group travelling to the Alps, the ski company would like a table and a chart to show the information as clearly as possible.
a) What sort of table can you suggest? Draw it accurately.
b) What sort of chart can you suggest? Draw it accurately.
c) What is the most common type of skier?

B	I	B	I	R	VG	I
I	R	G	VG	VG	B	B
I	I	B	B	R	B	G
I	B	G	G	I	I	I

Q3 Having seen the line graph opposite, a Quality Control Manager said "Admittedly we do have some complaints about our products, but from July complaints have tailed off, so our products must be of a better quality."
From the graph, do you think this statement is correct?
Why/Why not?

Probability

Probability can be a bit of a struggle — here's a quick reminder of the basics...

PROBABILITIES are always between 0 and 1

1) You should express probabilities as a <u>fraction</u> or a <u>decimal</u>.
2) A probability of <u>ZERO</u> means that it will <u>definitely not</u> happen.
3) A probability of <u>ONE</u> means it will <u>definitely</u> happen.

Q1 The number line opposite is a <u>probability scale</u>. Place the letters where you think the following statements lie, in terms of the <u>chance</u> of the event happening.

0   ½   1

a) The probability of getting a <u>head</u> on a toss of a 10p piece.
b) The probability of <u>choosing a red ball</u> from a bag containing 2 red balls and 1 green ball.
c) The probability of shaking a <u>five</u> on an ordinary dice.
d) The probability of choosing a <u>Guatemalan stamp</u> from a bag containing 60 British stamps and 40 French stamps.

Q2 Debbie's employer organises a weekly prize draw, where the winning employee is selected at random. Debbie only joins in if her chance of winning is at least 0.1. If there are 8 other people playing this week, will Debbie choose to play?

SHORTHAND NOTATION

1) <u>P(x) = 0.25</u> simply means "<u>the probability of event x happening is 0.25</u>".
2) Eg: if you roll a dice, the <u>probability of rolling</u> a 6 will be written as <u>P(rolls a 6)</u>.

Q3 After <u>49 tosses</u> of an unbiased coin, 24 have been heads and 25 have been tails. What is <u>P(50th toss will be a head)</u>?

Q4 If the probability of picking a banana from a fruit bowl is <u>0.27</u>, what is the probability of picking something which is <u>not</u> a banana?

Q5 A bag contains <u>3 red</u> balls, <u>4 blue</u> balls and <u>5 green</u> balls. A ball is chosen at random from the bag. What is the probability that:
a) it is green   c) it is red
b) it is blue   d) it is <u>not</u> red?

Q6 Students at school conduct a survey of the <u>colours</u> of parents' cars, where every parent owns one car. The table shows the results.

Red	Blue	Yellow	White	Green	Other
40	29	13	20	16	14

a) What is the probability of a parent owning a <u>red</u> car?
b) What is the probability of a parent owning a car that is <u>not</u> blue <u>or</u> green?

Q7 The probability of it raining during the monsoon is ¾, on a particular day.
a) What is the probability of it <u>not raining</u>?
b) If a monsoon 'season' lasts approximately <u>100 days</u>, how many days are likely to be <u>dry</u>?

Probability

Q8   Charlton is making a bet with his friend before the local cricket team play a match. He thinks the match will end in a draw. A local newspaper prints the team's results over their last 20 matches, as shown.

W	W	L	D	D	W	W	L	W	L
D	L	L	D	W	D	W	W	L	L

a) Complete the frequency table.

Outcome	Frequency
W	
D	
L	

b) Charlton reasons that since there are 3 possible results for any match, the probability that the next match will be drawn (D) is $\frac{1}{3}$. Explain why Charlton is wrong.

c) Suggest a value for the probability of a draw based on the team's past performance.

d) Based on their past performance, are the team most likely to win, lose, or draw?

Q9 **a)** What is the probability of randomly selecting either a black Ace or black King from an ordinary pack of playing cards?

b) If the entire suit of clubs is removed from a pack of cards, what is the probability of randomly selecting a red 7 from the remaining cards?

> Remember the OR rule — P(A or B) = P(A) + P(B).

c) If all the 7s are also removed from the pack of cards, what is the probability of randomly selecting the 4 of diamonds?

Q10   For the roulette wheel shown, the probability of the ball landing on each of the numbers is listed in the table below.

Number	1	2	3	4	5	6
Probability	$\frac{1}{6}$	$\frac{1}{3}$	$\frac{1}{6}$	$\frac{1}{12}$	$\frac{1}{12}$	$\frac{1}{6}$

a) Find the probability of landing on an even number.

b) What is the probability of landing on black?

c) Why is the probability of landing on a white or a 3 not $\frac{5}{12} + \frac{1}{6}$?

Q11   The notepad below shows orders for 4 different sorts of rice at a certain Indian restaurant. Based on this data, what is the probability that the next order of rice is:

a) for pilau rice?
b) for spicy mushroom or special fried rice?
c) not for boiled rice?

> If you're asked to work out probabilities based on some data, it's a <u>relative frequency</u> question.

boiled	20
pilau	24
spicy mushroom	10
special fried	6

Probability

Q12 There are 2 spinners: one with 3 sides numbered 1, 2, 3, and the other with 7 sides numbered 1, 2, 3, 4, 5, 6, 7.

a) If both are spun together, list all the possible outcomes.

b) Complete the following table showing the sum of the 2 numbers for each outcome.

	1	2	3	4	5	6	7
1							
2							
3							

c) What is the probability that the sum is 6?

d) What is the probability that the sum is even?

e) What is the probability that the sum is greater than or equal to 8?

f) What is the probability that the sum is less than 8?

g) Explain how you can work out the probability in part **f)** without using the table.

Q13 3 balls are drawn at random, without replacement, from a bag containing 4 green balls and 3 red balls.

a) Complete the tree diagram below showing all the possible outcomes and their probabilities.

For AND you MULTIPLY along the branches.
For OR you ADD the end results.

b) What is the probability that exactly 2 green balls are drawn?

c) What is the probability that the last ball drawn is the same colour as the first?

Probability

Q14 How many times must you roll an ordinary 6-sided dice for the probability of getting at least one 6 to be more than 0.5?

Don't forget the "at least" trick —
P(at least 1 six) = 1 – P(no sixes).

Q15 An unbiased dice in the shape of a tetrahedron has vertices numbered 1, 2, 3, 4. To win a game with this dice, you must throw a 4. At each go you have a maximum of 3 attempts.
a) Using a tree diagram, calculate the probability of winning with the second throw of the first go.
b) What is the probability of winning on the first go?

Q16 3 coins are drawn at random, without replacement, from a piggy bank containing 7 pound coins and 4 twenty-pence pieces.
a) Draw a tree diagram showing all possible outcomes and their probabilities.
b) Find the probability that the first coin selected is different in value from the third.
c) Find the probability that less than £1.50 is drawn altogether.

Q17 Fabrizio is practising taking penalties. The probability that he misses the goal completely is $\frac{1}{8}$. The probability that the goalkeeper saves the penalty is $\frac{3}{8}$. The probability that he scores is $\frac{1}{2}$. Fabrizio takes two penalties.

a) Calculate the probability that Fabrizio fails to score with his two penalties.
b) Calculate the probability that he scores only one goal.
c) Calculate the probability that Fabrizio scores on neither or both of his 2 attempts.

Q18 Trevor and his 2 brothers and 5 friends are seated at random in a row of 8 seats at the cinema. What is the probability that Trevor has one brother on his immediate left and one on his immediate right?

Careful here — you have to include the probability
that Trevor sits in one of the six middle seats.

Drawing a tree diagram might be a bit of a faff, but it can really help to make the question clearer. So if you're stuck, give the old tree diagram a try.

Types of Number

There are a few special number sequences that you really need to know — SQUARE, CUBE and PRIME NUMBERS, as well as POWERS and ODD and EVEN NUMBERS.

Q1 Sarah thinks of a number. She calculates that the square of the number is 256. What is the square root of the number?

Q2 On a certain day the temperature at midday was 14°C. By midnight the temperature had fallen by 17°C. What was the temperature at midnight?

Q3 1 is the first odd number. It is also the first square number and the first cube number. Which is greater: the third odd number, the third square number or the third cube number?

Q4 The following sequences are described in words. Write down their first four terms.
a) The prime numbers starting from 17.
b) The squares of odd numbers starting from $9^2 = 81$.

Q5 Using any or all of the figures **1, 2, 5, 9** write down:
a) the smallest prime number
b) a prime number greater than 20
c) a prime number between 10 and 20
d) two prime numbers whose sum is 21
e) a number that is not prime.

Remember — 1 is not a prime. Look, it just isn't, OK.

Q6 a) In the ten by ten square opposite, ring all the <u>prime numbers</u>. (The first three have been done for you.)
b) Among the prime numbers between 10 and 100, find three which are still prime when their digits are reversed.
c) Give a reason for 27 not being a prime number.

1	②	③	4	⑤	6	7	8	9	10
11	12	13	14	15	16	17	18	19	20
21	22	23	24	25	26	27	28	29	30
31	32	33	34	35	36	37	38	39	40
41	42	43	44	45	46	47	48	49	50
51	52	53	54	55	56	57	58	59	60
61	62	63	64	65	66	67	68	69	70
71	72	73	74	75	76	77	78	79	80
81	82	83	84	85	86	87	88	89	90
91	92	93	94	95	96	97	98	99	100

Q7 What is the largest prime less than 120?

Q8 How many prime numbers are even?

Powers

Hang on there. Before you try this page, make sure you know all the rules for dealing with powers...

The small number is called the <u>power</u> or <u>index number.</u> Remember the plural of index is <u>indices.</u>

$5^4 = 5 \times 5 \times 5 \times 5 = \underline{625}$

we say "five to the power four"

$8^3 = 8 \times 8 \times 8 = \underline{512}$

we say "eight to the power three" or "eight cubed"

Q1   Complete the following:
a) $2^4 = 2 \times 2 \times 2 \times 2$ =
b) $10^3 = 10 \times 10 \times 10$ =
c) $3^5 = 3 \times ...$ =
d) $4^6 = 4 \times ...$ =
e) $1^9 = 1 \times ...$ =
f) $5^6 = 5 \times ...$ =

Q2   Simplify the following:
a) $2 \times 2 \times 2 \times 2 \times 2 \times 2 \times 2 \times 2$
b) $12 \times 12 \times 12 \times 12 \times 12$
c) $x \times x \times x \times x \times x \times x$
d) $m \times m \times m$
e) $y \times y \times y \times y$
f) $z \times z \times z \times z \times z \times z$

Q3   Complete the following (the first one has been done for you):
a) $10^2 \times 10^3 = (10 \times 10) \times (10 \times 10 \times 10)$ $= 10^5$
b) $10^3 \times 10^4 =$ =
c) $10^4 \times 10^2 =$ =
d) $10^5 \times 10^3 =$ =
e) What is the <u>quick method</u> for writing down the final result in **b)**, **c)** and **d)**?

Easy — you'll have learnt this from your power rules.

Q4   Complete the following (the first one has been done for you):
a) $2^4 \div 2^2 = \dfrac{(2 \times 2 \times 2 \times 2)}{(2 \times 2)} = 2^2$
c) $4^5 \div 4^3 = \dfrac{(4 \times 4 \times 4 \times 4 \times 4)}{} =$
b) $2^5 \div 2^2 = \dfrac{(2 \times 2 \times 2 \times 2 \times 2)}{(2 \times 2)} =$
d) $8^5 \div 8^2 =$ =

e) What is the quick method for writing down the final result in **b)**, **c)** and **d)**?

Q5   Which of the following are <u>true</u>?
a) $2^4 \times 2^6 = 2^{10}$
b) $2^2 \times 2^3 \times 2^4 = 2^9$
c) $2^3 \times 2^2 = 2^6$
d) $4^{10} \times 4^4 \times 4^2 = 4^{18}$
e) $2^1 \times 2^3 \times 2^4 = 2^8$
f) $10^4 \times 10^2 = 10^8$
g) $2^{20} \div 2^5 = 2^4$
h) $3^{12} \div 3^4 = 3^8$
i) $4^6 \div 6^4 = 4^2$
j) $10^{20} \div 10^3 = 10^{17}$
k) $4^6 \div (4^2 \times 4^3) = 4^1$
l) $9^2 \times (9^{30} \div 9^{25}) = 9^{10}$

Powers

Powers questions are great fun once you've learned the
magical power laws. Without them you'll be as clueless as
Mr Clueless from planet Clueless trying to hitchhike to Clueville.

Q6 Remove the brackets from the following and express as a single power:
a) $(3^4 \times 3^2) \div (3^6 \times 3^3)$
d) $(3^6)^{-2}$
b) $(4^{10} \times 4^{12}) \times 4^3$
e) $4^2 \times 4^{-1} \times 4^6 \times (4^2 \div 4^3)$
c) $10^2 \div (10^3 \times 10^{12})$
f) $(5^2 \times 5^3) \div (5^6 \div 5^4)$

Q7 Write the following as a <u>single term</u>:

a) $10^6 \div 10^4$
d) $x^2 \times x^3$
b) $(8^2 \times 8^5) \div 8^3$
e) $a^5 \times a^4$
c) $6^{10} \div (6^2 \times 6^3)$
f) $p^4 \times p^5 \times p^6$

Q8 Which of the following are <u>true</u>?

a) $2^{-3} = 1/6$
c) $4^{-2} = 1/16$
e) $1/9 = 3^2$
b) $17^0 = 0$
d) $1^{-17} = 1$
f) $28^0 = 1$

Q9 Write the following as a single power:

a) $6^3 \times 6^5 \times 6^{-4}$
e) $16^3 \times 4^{-3} \div 4^4$
b) $(6^3)^2$
f) $(3^2)^4 \div (3^3)^3$
c) $2^0 \times 2^{-3} \times 4^2$
g) $(25^1)^3 \div (5^3)$
d) $3^4 \div 3^5 \times 3^3$
h) $2^3 \div 16^{-3}$

Some of these are pretty tricky
— do them in <u>stages</u> using one
power law each time.

Q10 Work out these nasty beasties.

a) 4^0
d) 10^{-3}
g) $8^{-\frac{1}{3}}$
j) $3^3 \times 4^0$
b) 35^1
e) $5^2 \div 2^{-2}$
h) $125^{-\frac{1}{3}}$
k) $4^{\frac{3}{2}}$
c) 2^{-1}
f) $16^{-1} \times 4^2 \times 2^4$
i) $25^{\frac{1}{2}}$
l)

Q11 Now work out these beastly nasties:
a) $\left(\frac{2}{3}\right)^2$
b) $\left(\frac{3}{5}\right)^3$
c) $\left(\frac{27}{8}\right)^{\frac{2}{3}}$
d) $\left(\frac{4}{25}\right)^{-\frac{1}{2}}$
e) $\left(\frac{8}{1000}\right)^{\frac{2}{3}}$

Manipulating Surds and Use of π

Well, to be honest, I think the idea of rational and irrational numbers is a bit odd. Basically, a <u>rational</u> number is either a <u>whole</u> number or one you can write as a <u>fraction</u>. An <u>irrational</u> number... you guessed it... is <u>not</u> whole and <u>can't</u> be written as a fraction.

Q1   Write down a rational number and an irrational number both greater than $\sqrt{5}$ and less than 5.

Q2   Write down a value of x for which $x^{\frac{1}{2}}$ is:
a) irrational
b) rational

Watch out for those roots — they're not always irrational. For example, the square root of a square number will be rational.

Q3   Which of the following powers of $\sqrt{3}$ are rational and which are irrational?

a) $\left(\sqrt{3}\right)^1$ **c)** $\left(\sqrt{3}\right)^3$

b) $\left(\sqrt{3}\right)^2$ **d)** $\left(\sqrt{3}\right)^4$

Q4   Five of the following numbers are rational and five are irrational:

$$\sqrt{2}\times\sqrt{8},\ \left(\sqrt{5}\right)^6,\ \sqrt{3}/\sqrt{2},\ \left(\sqrt{7}\right)^3,\ 6\pi,\ 0.4,\ \sqrt{5}-2.1,\ 40-2^{-1}-4^{-2},\ 49^{-\frac{1}{2}},\ \sqrt{6}+6$$

a) Write down the five rational numbers.
b) Write down the five irrational numbers.

Q5   Which of the following are rational and which are irrational?
a) $16^{\frac{1}{2}}$ **b)** $16^{\frac{1}{3}}$ **c)** $16^{\frac{1}{4}}$

Q6   Give an example of two different irrational numbers, x and y, where x/y is a rational number.

Q7   **a)** Write down a rational number which is greater than 1 but less than 2.
       b) Write down an irrational number which lies between 1 and 2.
       c) If P is a non-zero rational number, is $1/P$ also a rational number?
           Clearly show your reasoning.

Don't forget that recurring decimals, like 0.333333333, can be put into fraction form, like $\frac{1}{3}$ — so they're rational too.

Manipulating Surds and Use of π

Q8 If $x = 2$, $y = \sqrt{3}$ and $z = 2\sqrt{2}$, which of the following expressions are rational and which are irrational? Show your working.

a) xyz

b) $(xyz)^2$

c) $x + yz$

d) $\dfrac{yz}{2\sqrt{3x}}$

Q9 A circle has a radius of $\sqrt{3}$ cm. What is its exact area? (Area of circle = πr^2.)

Q10 Simplify:

> Remember — $\sqrt{a} \times \sqrt{b} = \sqrt{(ab)}$.

a) $\sqrt{5} \times \sqrt{3}$

b) $\dfrac{\sqrt{20}}{\sqrt{5}}$

c) $\sqrt{4} - \sqrt{1}$

d) $\left(\dfrac{\sqrt{5}}{\sqrt{2}}\right)^2$

e) $\left(\sqrt{x}\right)^2$

f) $\sqrt{x^2}$

g) $\sqrt{8} \times \sqrt{8}$

h) $\sqrt{18} - \sqrt{9}$

Q11 Are the following expressions rational or irrational?

a) $(1+\sqrt{5})(1-\sqrt{5})$

b) $\dfrac{1+\sqrt{5}}{1-\sqrt{5}}$

Q12 If $x = 1$ and $y = \sqrt{2}$, are the following expressions rational or irrational?

a) $(x + y)(x - y)$

b) $\dfrac{x+y}{x-y}$

Q13 Rationalise the denominators of the following expressions, and then simplify if necessary.

a) $\dfrac{1}{\sqrt{2}}$

b) $\dfrac{2}{\sqrt{8}}$

c) $\dfrac{a}{\frac{\sqrt{40}}{2}}$

d) $\dfrac{x}{\sqrt{xy}}$

e) $\dfrac{1}{1+\sqrt{2}}$

f) $\dfrac{6}{3+\sqrt{3}}$

g) $\dfrac{2}{1+\sqrt{6}}$

h) $\dfrac{5+\sqrt{5}}{5-\sqrt{5}}$

> Remember: rationalising the denominator means getting rid of the square root signs on the bottom of fractions.

UNIT 2 — NUMBER AND ALGEBRA

Multiples, Factors and Primes

Q1   1   3   6   9   12
From the numbers above, write down:
a) a multiple of 4
b) the prime number
c) two square numbers
d) three factors of 27
e) two numbers, P and Q, that satisfy both P = 2Q and P = $\sqrt{144}$

This is real basic stuff —
you just have to know
your times tables. And
your primes, of course...

Q2   48 students went on a geography field trip
Their teachers split them into equal groups
Suggest five different ways that the teachers
might have split up the students.

Q3   A school ran 3 evening classes: Conversational French, Cake Making and Woodturning.
The Conversational French class had 29 students, Cake Making had 27 students, and the
Woodturning class had 23. For which classes did the teacher have difficulty dividing the
students into equal groups?

Q4   a) Write down the first five cube numbers.
b) Which of the numbers given in part a) are multiples of 2?
c) Which of the numbers given in part a) are multiples of 3?
d) Which of the numbers given in part a) are multiples of 4?
e) Which of the numbers given in part a) are multiples of 5?

Q5   Write down the prime factorisation of:
a) 18
b) 140
c) 47

The tricky bit is remembering that a <u>prime factorisation</u>
includes <u>all</u> the prime factors that multiply to make that
number — so you've got to repeat some of them.

Q6   a) List the first five prime numbers.
b) If added together, what is their total?
c) Write down the prime factorisation of the answer to part **b)**.

Q7   a) List the first five odd numbers.
b) If added together, what is their total?
c) Write down the prime factorisation of the answer to part **b)**.

Multiples, Factors and Primes

Q8 The prime factorisation of a certain number is $3^2 \times 5 \times 11$.
   a) Write down the number.
   b) Write down the prime factorisation of 165.

Q9 **a)** Write down the first ten square numbers.
   b) From your list pick out all the multiples of 2.
   c) From your list pick out all the multiples of 3.
   d) From your list pick out any cube numbers.
   e) Add the first five square numbers together and
     write down the prime factorisation of the total.

Q10 Gordon is doing some woodwork and needs to calculate
   the volume of a wooden rectangular block (a cuboid).
   The length of the block is 50 cm, the height 25 cm and the width 16 cm.
   a) What is the volume (in cm³) of the wooden block?
   b) What is the prime factorisation of the number found in part **a)**?

   c) Gordon needs to cut the block into smaller blocks with dimensions 4 cm × 5 cm × 5 cm.
     What is the maximum number of small blocks Gordon can make from the larger block?
     Make sure you show all your working.

Q11 The prime factorisation of a certain number is $2^3 \times 5 \times 17$.
   a) What is the number?
   b) What is the prime factorisation of half of this number?
   c) What is the prime factorisation of a quarter of the number?
   d) What is the prime factorisation of an eighth of the number?

Q12 Bryan and Sue were playing a guessing game. Sue thought of a number
   between 1 and 100 which Bryan had to guess. Bryan was allowed to ask five
   questions, which are listed with Sue's responses in the table below.

Bryan's Questions	Sue's Responses
Is it prime?	No
Is it odd?	No
Is it less than 50?	Yes
Is it a multiple of 3?	Yes
Is it a multiple of 7?	Yes

Start by writing down
a number table up to 100.
Look at each response in
turn and cross off numbers
'till you've only got
one left.

What is the number that Sue thought of?

LCM and HCF

Millom Home Top tip

These two fancy names always put people off — but really they're dead easy. Just learn these simple facts:

1) The Lowest Common Multiple (LCM) is the SMALLEST number that will DIVIDE BY ALL the numbers in question.

E.g.   3, 6, 9, 12, 15 are all multiples of 3.
         5, 10, 15, 20, 25 are all multiples of 5.
         The lowest number that is in both lists is 15, so 15 is the LCM of 3 and 5.

2) The Highest Common Factor (HCF) is the BIGGEST number that will DIVIDE INTO ALL the numbers in question.

E.g. 1, 2, 4, 8 are all factors of 8.
       1, 2, 3, 4, 6, 12 are all factors of 12.
       The highest number that is in both lists is 4, so 4 is the HCF of 8 and 12.

Q1 **a)** List the <u>first ten</u> multiples of 6, <u>starting at 6</u>.
        b) List the <u>first ten</u> multiples of 5, <u>starting at 5</u>.
        c) What is the <u>LCM</u> of 5 and 6?

I tell you what, it's a lot easier to find the LCM or HCF once you've listed the multiples or factors. If you miss out this step it'll all go horribly wrong, believe me.

Q2 **a)** List all the factors of 30.
        b) List all the factors of 48.
        c) What is the <u>HCF</u> of 30 and 48?

Q3 For each set of numbers find the HCF.
        a) 40, 60   **d)** 15, 45   **g)** 32, 64
        b) 10, 40, 60   **e)** 15, 30, 45   **h)** 32, 48, 64
        c) 10, 24, 40, 60 **f)** 15, 20, 30, 45 **i)** 16, 32, 48, 64

Q4 For each set of numbers find the LCM.
        a) 40, 60   **d)** 15, 45   **g)** 32, 64
        b) 10, 40, 60   **e)** 15, 30, 45   **h)** 32, 48, 64
        c) 10, 24, 40, 60 **f)** 15, 20, 30, 45 **i)** 16, 32, 48, 64

Q5 Lars, Rita and Alan regularly go swimming. Lars goes every 2 days, Rita goes every 3 days and Alan goes every 5 days. They <u>all</u> went swimming together on Friday 1st June.

This is just a LCM question in disguise.

        a) On what <u>date</u> will Lars and Rita next go swimming together?
        b) On what <u>date</u> will Rita and Alan next go swimming together?
        c) On what <u>day of the week</u> will all 3 next go swimming together?
        d) Which of the 3 (if any) will go swimming on 15th June?

Fractions, Decimals and Percentages

I reckon that converting decimals to percentages is about as easy as it gets — so make the most of it.

Q1 Express each of the following as a percentage:

a) 0.25   c) 0.75   e) 0.4152   g) 0.3962
b) 0.5   d) 0.1   f) 0.8406   h) 0.2828

All you're doing is multiplying by 100 — it really couldn't be easier.

Q2 Express each percentage as a decimal:

a) 50%   c) 40%   e) 60.2%   g) 43.1%
b) 12%   d) 34%   f) 54.9%   h) 78.8%

Now you're dividing by 100 — so just move the decimal point to the left.

Q3 Express each of the following as a percentage:

a) $\frac{1}{2}$ e) $\frac{1}{25}$

b) $\frac{1}{4}$ f) $\frac{2}{3}$

c) $\frac{1}{8}$ g) $\frac{4}{15}$

d) $\frac{3}{4}$ h) $\frac{2}{7}$

Q4 Express each percentage as a fraction in its lowest terms:

a) 25%   e) 8.2%
b) 60%   f) 49.6%
c) 45%   g) 88.6%
d) 30%   h) 32.4%

Best thing to do with e)-h) is to put them over 100, then get rid of the decimal point by multiplying top and bottom by 10. Then just cancel down as normal.

Q5 119 out of 140 houses on an estate have DVD players. What percentage is this?

Q6 In an exam Tina scored 52/80. The grade she receives depends on the percentage scored. What grade will Tina get?

Grades	
51-60%	D
61-70%	C
71-80%	B
81-90%	A
91-100%	A*

Fractions, Decimals and Percentages

 <u>Decimals</u> are just another way of writing <u>fractions</u> — so it's easy to convert between the two...

Q7 Without using a calculator, write the following fractions as decimals:

a) $\dfrac{3}{10}$
b) $\dfrac{37}{100}$
c) $\dfrac{2}{5}$
d) $\dfrac{3}{8}$

e) $\dfrac{14}{8}$
f) $\dfrac{8}{64}$
g) $\dfrac{24}{40}$
h) $\dfrac{4}{80}$

Q8 Fill in the gaps in the following conversion table :

Fraction	Decimal
½	0.5
⅕	
	0.125
	1.6
⁴⁄16	
⁷⁄2	
	0.x
ˣ⁄100	
³⁄20	
	0.45

Q9 Write the following fractions as recurring decimals:

a) $\dfrac{5}{9}$
b) $\dfrac{7}{9}$
c) $\dfrac{7}{11}$
d) $\dfrac{47}{99}$

e) $\dfrac{10}{11}$
f) $\dfrac{29}{99}$
g) $\dfrac{478}{999}$
h) $\dfrac{589}{999}$

Q10 Write the following decimals as fractions in their lowest form:

a) 0.6
b) 0.75
c) 0.95
d) 0.128

e) $0.\dot{3}$
f) $0.\dot{6}$
g) $0.\dot{1}$

Q11 Write the following recurring decimals as fractions in their lowest form:

a) 0.222...
b) 0.444...
c) 0.888...
d) 0.808080...

e) 0.121212...
f) 0.545545545...
g) 0.753753753...
h) 0.156156156...

Fractions

Answer the following questions without using a calculator.

Q1 Carry out the following multiplications, giving your answers in their lowest terms:

a) $\dfrac{1}{8} \times \dfrac{1}{8}$

b) $\dfrac{2}{3} \times \dfrac{1}{6}$

c) $\dfrac{3}{18} \times \dfrac{1}{3}$

d) $1\dfrac{1}{4} \times 3\dfrac{1}{8}$

e) $1\dfrac{1}{4} \times 4\dfrac{1}{8}$

f) $\dfrac{9}{10} \times \dfrac{9}{100} \times \dfrac{1}{100}$

Q2 Carry out the following divisions, giving your answers in their lowest terms:

a) $\dfrac{1}{8} \div \dfrac{1}{8}$

b) $\dfrac{2}{3} \div \dfrac{1}{6}$

c) $\dfrac{3}{18} \div \dfrac{1}{3}$

d) $1\dfrac{1}{4} \div 3\dfrac{1}{8}$

e) $1\dfrac{1}{4} \div 4\dfrac{1}{8}$

f) $\left(\dfrac{9}{10} \div \dfrac{9}{100}\right) \div \dfrac{1}{100}$

Q3 Evaluate the following, giving your answers in their lowest terms:

a) $\dfrac{1}{8} + \dfrac{1}{8}$

b) $\dfrac{1}{6} + \dfrac{2}{3}$

c) $\dfrac{3}{18} + \dfrac{1}{3}$

d) $1\dfrac{1}{4} + 3\dfrac{1}{8}$

e) $1\dfrac{1}{4} + 4\dfrac{1}{8}$

f) $\dfrac{9}{10} + \dfrac{9}{100} + \dfrac{1}{100}$

Q4 Caley is making some punch for her birthday party. She mixes $\dfrac{1}{2}$ litre of cranberry juice, $1\dfrac{1}{2}$ litres of apple juice, $\dfrac{2}{3}$ litre of orange juice and $\dfrac{4}{5}$ litres of pineapple juice.

She has a bowl that will hold 4 litres. Will this be big enough to contain all of the punch?

Q5 Evaluate the following, giving your answers in their lowest terms:

a) $\dfrac{1}{8} - \dfrac{1}{8}$

b) $\dfrac{2}{3} - \dfrac{1}{6}$

c) $\dfrac{3}{18} - \dfrac{1}{3}$

d) $3\dfrac{1}{8} - 1\dfrac{1}{4}$

e) $1\dfrac{1}{8} - 4\dfrac{1}{4}$

f) $\left(\dfrac{9}{10} - \dfrac{9}{100}\right) - \dfrac{1}{100}$

Q6 Evaluate the following, giving your answers in their lowest terms:

a) $\dfrac{1}{2} + \dfrac{1}{4}$

b) $\dfrac{2}{3} - \dfrac{1}{4}$

c) $\dfrac{1}{5} + \dfrac{2}{3} - \dfrac{2}{5}$

d) $5 - \dfrac{1}{4}$

e) $6 \times \dfrac{2}{3}$

f) $\dfrac{4}{5} \div \dfrac{2}{3}$

g) $\dfrac{5}{12} \times \dfrac{3}{2}$

h) $\dfrac{5}{6} - \dfrac{7}{8}$

i) $3 + \dfrac{8}{5}$

j) $\dfrac{2}{3}\left(\dfrac{3}{4} + \dfrac{4}{5}\right)$

k) $\left(\dfrac{1}{7} + \dfrac{3}{14}\right) \times \left(3 - \dfrac{1}{5}\right)$

l) $\left(\dfrac{3}{4} - \dfrac{1}{5}\right) \div \left(\dfrac{7}{8} + \dfrac{1}{16}\right)$

Fractions

The cunning bit with long wordy questions is picking out the important bits and then translating them into numbers. It's not that easy at first, but you'll get better — I guess you've just gotta learn to ignore the waffly stuff.

Answer these without using your calculator:

Q7 What fraction of 1 hour is:
a) 5 minutes
b) 15 minutes
c) 40 minutes?

Q8 If a TV programme lasts 40 minutes, what fraction of the programme is left after:
a) 10 minutes
b) 15 minutes
c) 35 minutes?

Q9 A café employs eighteen girls and twelve boys to wait at tables. Another six boys and nine girls work in the kitchen.
What fraction of the <u>kitchen staff</u> are girls?
What fraction of the <u>employees</u> are boys?

Q10

In a survey, people were asked if they liked a new cola drink. One in five thought it was great, four out of fifteen felt there was no difference in taste, three in ten disliked it and <u>the rest</u> offered no opinion.
What fraction of people offered no opinion?

Forget all about cola drinks and red trousers — just write it all as a sum, then do the calculation. Nowt to it.

Q11 Neil wore red trousers on a total of 12 days in November.
a) On what fraction of the total number of days in November did Neil wear <u>red trousers</u>?
b) For 1/5 of the days in November Neil wore a <u>blue shirt</u>. How many days is this?

Q12

The Sandwich Club of Great Britain are going on their annual picnic.
a) The boxes they use to transport their sandwiches are 10 inches high and are the width of a single sandwich. Each sandwich is 5/8 inch thick. How many boxes will they need for 80 sandwiches?
b) How tall would the box need to be if <u>40</u> sandwiches were to be stacked inside?

Ratios

Answer these without using your calculator:

Q1 Divide the following amounts in the ratios given:
- **a)** £20 in the ratio 2:3
- **b)** 150 m in the ratio 8:7
- **c)** 500 g in the ratio 1:2:2
- **d)** 18 hrs in the ratio 1:2:3

For these you add up the ratio numbers to find the total number of parts and <u>divide</u> by this. Then <u>multiply</u> by each number in the ratio separately to find the different amounts.

Q2
- **a)** <u>Increase</u> £3.20 in the ratio 2:3.
- **b)** <u>Decrease</u> 120 cm in the ratio 3:2.

Q3 John and Peter share a bar of chocolate marked into 16 squares. They share it in the ratio 1:3 respectively. How many squares does each boy get?

Q4 A 2 litre bottle of cola is to be shared between three girls in the ratio 2:3:5. How many <u>millilitres</u> will each girl get?

<u>Watch out for your units</u> — you'll have to change them over for this one — and your answer should be in <u>millilitres</u>.

Q5 Tony gives £100 to be shared by Jane, Holly and Rosemary in a ratio according to their <u>age</u>. Jane is 10, Holly is 12 and Rosemary is 3 years old. How much will each child get?

Q6 Sunil and Paul work in a restaurant. As they work different hours, they split their tips in the ratio 3:4. One night they got £28 in tips between them. Who got the most money from the tips and how much did they get?

Q7 Sarah works as a waitress. Each week, she splits her wage into spending money and savings in the ratio 7:3.
- **a)** One week, Sarah earns £130.
  How much should she put in her savings that week?
- **b)** The next week, Sarah put £42 into her savings.
  How much did she earn in total that week?

Q8 Concrete is mixed using cement, sand and gravel in the ratio 1:3:6. If Dave uses a 5 kg bag of cement, how much:
- **a)** sand does he need?
- **b)** gravel does he need?
- **c)** If Dave needs 80 kg of concrete, how much of each substance does he need?

Basic Algebra

Q1 Work out the following temperature changes:
a) 20 °C to -7 °C
c) -17 °C to -5 °C
e) -31 °C to -16 °C
b) -10 °C to -32 °C
d) -3 °C to 15 °C
f) -5 °C to -17 °C

Q2 Which is larger and by how much?
a) -12 + 7 – 4 + 6 – 2 + 7 or **b)** -30 + 26 – 3 – 7 + 17

Q3 Simplify: **a)** $4x - 5x + 3x - x + 2x - 7x$ **b)** $30y - 10y + 2y - 3y + 4y - 5y$

Q4 Find the value of xy and $\dfrac{x}{y}$ for each of the following:
a) $x = -100$ $y = 10$
c) $x = -48$ $y = -3$
b) $x = 24$ $y = -4$
d) $x = 0$ $y = -4$

Q5 Find the value of $(a - b) \div (c + d)$ when $a = 10$, $b = -26$, $c = -5$ and $d = -4$.

Q6 Simplify the following:

a) $2x \times -3y$
d) $4p \times -4p$
g) $10x \div -2y$
j) $70x^2 \div -7x^2$
b) $-8a \times 2b$
e) $-30x \div -3y$
h) $-30x \div -10x$
k) $-36x^2 \div -9x$
c) $-4x \times -2x$
f) $50x \div -5y$
i) $40ab \div -10ab$
l) $40y^2 \div -5y$

Q7 Simplify the following by collecting like terms together:

a) $3x^2 + 4x + 12x^2 - 5x$
f) $15ab - 10a + b - 7a + 2ba$
b) $14x^2 - 10x - x^2 + 5x$
g) $4pq - 14p - 8q + p - q + 8p$
c) $12 - 4x^2 + 10x - 3x^2 + 2x$
h) $13x^2 + 4x^2 - 5y^2 + y^2 - x^2$
d) $20abc + 12ab + 10bac + 4b$
i) $11ab + 2cd - ba - 13dc + abc$
e) $8pq + 7p + q + 10qp - q + p$
j) $3x^2 + 4xy + 2y^2 - z^2 + 2xy - y^2 - 5x^2$

Eeeek — loads
of questions...

UNIT 2 — NUMBER AND ALGEBRA

Basic Algebra

Remember FOIL for multiplying brackets... don't want to miss any terms now, do you...

Q8 Multiply out the brackets and simplify where possible:

a) $4(x + y - z)$

b) $x(x + 5)$

c) $-3(x - 2)$

d) $7(a + b) + 2(a + b)$

e) $3(a + 2b) - 2(2a + b)$

f) $4(x - 2) - 2(x - 1)$

g) $4e(e + 2f) + 2f(e - f)$

h) $14(2m - n) + 2(3n - 6m)$

i) $4x(x + 2) - 2x(3 - x)$

j) $3(2 + ab) + 5(1 - ab)$

k) $(x - 2y)z - 2x(x + z)$

l) $4(x - 2y) - (5 + x - 2y)$

m) $a - 4(a + b)$

n) $4pq(2 + r) + 5qr(2p + 7)$

o) $x^2(x + 1)$

p) $4x^2\left(x + 2 + \dfrac{1}{x}\right)$

q) $8ab(a + 3 + b)$

r) $7pq\left(p + q - \dfrac{1}{p}\right)$

s) $4[(x + y) - 3(y - x)]$

Q9 For each of the large rectangles below, write down the area of each of the small rectangles and hence find an expression for the area of each large rectangle.

a)

b)

c)

Q10 Multiply out the brackets and simplify your answers where possible:

a) $(x - 3)(x + 1)$

b) $(x - 3)(x + 5)$

c) $(x + 10)(x + 3)$

d) $(x - 5)(x - 2)$

e) $(x + 2)(x - 7)$

f) $(4 - x)(7 - x)$

g) $(2 + 3x)(3x - 1)$

h) $(3x + 2)(2x - 4)$

i) $(x - 3)(4x + 1)$

j) $2(2x + y)(x - 2y)$

k) $4(x + 2y)(3x - 2y)$

l) $(3x + 2y)^2$

Q11 Find the product of $5x - 2$ and $3x + 2$.

Q12 Find the square of $2x - 1$.

Q13 A rectangular pond has length $(3x - 2)$ m and width $(5 - x)$ m.
Write down a simplified expression for:

a) the pond's perimeter

b) the pond's area.

Basic Algebra

Q14 A rectangular bar of chocolate consists of 20 small rectangular pieces. The size of a small rectangular piece of chocolate is 2 cm by x cm.

   a) Write down an expression for the perimeter of the whole bar.
   b) Write down an expression for the area of the whole bar.
   c) If I ate 6 small rectangular pieces of chocolate, what is the area of the remaining bar?

Q15 Find a simplified expression for the perimeter *and* the area of the following shapes.

   a)   **b)**   **c)**   **d)**

Q16 Using the fact that $a^2 - b^2 = (a + b)(a - b)$, factorise the following expressions:

   a) $x^2 - 9$ **d)** $36 - a^2$ **g)** $25 - 16z^2$ **j)** $x^4 - y^4$
   b) $y^2 - 16$ **e)** $4x^2 - 9$ **h)** $1 - 36a^2$ **k)** $1 - (ab)^2$
   c) $25 - z^2$ **f)** $9y^2 - 4$ **i)** $x^4 - 36$ **l)** $100\,x^2 - 144y^2$

Q17 Factorise:

   a) $x^2 - 4$ **b)** $144 - y^4$ **c)** $1 - 9x^2y^2$ **d)** $49x^4y^4 - 1$

Q18 All the expressions below have a^2 as a common factor. Factorise each of them.

   a) $a^2b + a^2c$ **d)** $a^3 + a^2y$
   b) $5a^2 + 13a^2b$ **e)** $2a^2x + 3a^2y + 4a^2z$
   c) $2a^2b + 3a^2c$ **f)** $a^2b^2 + a^3c^2$

Q19 Factorise and simplify the following:

   a) $4xyz + 8xyz$ **b)** $8xyz + 12xyz$ **c)** $8xyz + 16x^2yz$ **d)** $20x^2y^2z^2 + 16xyz^2$

Algebraic Fractions

Q1   Simplify the following by cancelling down where possible:

a) $\dfrac{27x^4y^2z}{9x^3yz^2}$

b) $\dfrac{48a^2b^2}{(2a)^2c}$

c) $\dfrac{3xyz}{9x^2y^3z^4}$

d) $\dfrac{4p^3q^3}{(2pr)^3}$

Q2   Multiply out the following, leaving your answers as simplified as possible:

a) $\dfrac{x^2}{y}\times\dfrac{2}{x^3}$

b) $\dfrac{3a^4}{2}\times\dfrac{b}{a^2}$

c) $\dfrac{2x}{y^2}\times\dfrac{y^3}{4x^3}$

d) $\dfrac{3pq}{2}\times\dfrac{4r^2}{9p}$

e) $\dfrac{10z^3}{xy}\times\dfrac{4x^3}{5z}$

f) $\dfrac{30a^2b^2c^2}{7}\times\dfrac{21c^2}{ab^3}$

g) $\dfrac{4}{x}\times\dfrac{x^3}{2}\times\dfrac{x}{10}$

h) $\dfrac{2a^2}{3}\times\dfrac{9b}{a}\times\dfrac{2a^2b}{5}$

i) $\dfrac{5a^2b}{b}\times\dfrac{3a^2c^3}{10bd}$

j) $\dfrac{p^2}{pq^2}\times\dfrac{q^2}{p}$

k) $\dfrac{90r^2}{14t}\times\dfrac{7t^3}{30r}$

l) $\dfrac{400d^4}{51e^5}\times\dfrac{102d^2e^4}{800e^2f}$

It helps if you can cancel some factors before multiplying.

Q3   Divide the following, leaving your answer as simplified as possible:

a) $\dfrac{4x^3}{y}\div\dfrac{2x}{y^2}$

b) $\dfrac{ab}{c}\div\dfrac{b}{c}$

c) $\dfrac{30x^3}{y^2}\div\dfrac{10x}{y}$

d) $\dfrac{pq}{r}\div\dfrac{2}{r}$

e) $\dfrac{e^2f^2}{5}\div\dfrac{ef}{10}$

f) $\dfrac{5x^3}{y}\div\dfrac{1}{y}$

g) $\dfrac{16xyz}{3}\div\dfrac{4x^2}{9}$

h) $\dfrac{20a^3}{b^3}\div\dfrac{5}{b^2}$

i) $\dfrac{25a^3}{b^3}\div\dfrac{5}{b^2}$

j) $\dfrac{4x}{y^4z^4}\div\dfrac{2}{y^2z^3}$

k) $\dfrac{3m}{2n^2}\div\dfrac{m}{4n}$

l) $\dfrac{70f^3}{g}\div\dfrac{10f^4}{g^2}$

Q4   Solve the following equations for x:

a) $\dfrac{20x^4y^2z^3}{7xy^5}\times\dfrac{14y^3}{40x^2z^3}=5$

b) $\dfrac{48x^5y^2}{12z^3}\div\dfrac{16x^2y^2}{z^3}=2$

Algebraic Fractions

OK, I guess it gets a bit tricky here — you've got to cross-multiply to get a common denominator before you can get anywhere with adding or subtracting.

Q5 Add the following, simplifying your answers:

a) $\dfrac{3}{2x} + \dfrac{y}{2x}$

b) $\dfrac{1}{x} + \dfrac{y}{x}$

c) $\dfrac{4xy}{3z} + \dfrac{2xy}{3z}$

d) $\dfrac{(4x+2)}{3} + \dfrac{(2x-1)}{3}$

e) $\dfrac{5x+2}{x} + \dfrac{2x+4}{x}$

f) $\dfrac{6x}{3} + \dfrac{2x+y}{6}$

g) $\dfrac{x}{8} + \dfrac{2+y}{24}$

h) $\dfrac{x}{10} + \dfrac{y-1}{5}$

i) $\dfrac{2x}{3} + \dfrac{2x}{4}$

j) $\dfrac{x}{6} + \dfrac{5x}{7}$

k) $\dfrac{x}{3} + \dfrac{x}{y}$

l) $\dfrac{zx}{4} + \dfrac{x+z}{y}$

Q6 Subtract the following, leaving your answers as simplified as possible:

a) $\dfrac{4x}{3} - \dfrac{5y}{3}$

b) $\dfrac{4x+3}{y} - \dfrac{4}{y}$

c) $\dfrac{(8x+3y)}{2x} - \dfrac{(4x+2)}{2x}$

d) $\dfrac{(9-5x)}{3x} - \dfrac{(3+x)}{3x}$

e) $\dfrac{10+x^2}{4x} - \dfrac{x^2+11}{4x}$

f) $\dfrac{2x}{3} - \dfrac{y}{6}$

g) $\dfrac{z}{5} - \dfrac{2z}{15}$

h) $\dfrac{4m}{n} - \dfrac{m}{3}$

i) $\dfrac{2b}{a} - \dfrac{b}{7}$

j) $\dfrac{(p+q)}{2} - \dfrac{3p}{5}$

k) $\dfrac{p-2q}{4} - \dfrac{2p+q}{2}$

l) $\dfrac{3x}{y} - \dfrac{4-x}{3}$

Q7 Simplify the following:

a) $\left(\dfrac{a}{b} \div \dfrac{c}{d}\right) \times \dfrac{ac}{bd}$

b) $\dfrac{x^2+xy}{x} \times \dfrac{z}{xz+yz}$

c) $\dfrac{(p+q)}{r} \times \dfrac{3}{2(p+q)}$

d) $\dfrac{m^2n}{p} + \dfrac{mn}{p^2}$

e) $\dfrac{1}{x+y} + \dfrac{1}{x-y}$

f) $\dfrac{2}{x} - \dfrac{3}{2x} + \dfrac{4}{3x}$

g) $\dfrac{a+b}{a-b} + \dfrac{a-b}{a+b}$

h) $\dfrac{1}{4pq} \div \dfrac{1}{3pq}$

i) $\dfrac{x}{8} - \dfrac{x+y}{4} + \dfrac{x-y}{2}$

Solving Equations

Q1 When 1 is added to a number and the answer then trebled, it gives the same result as doubling the number and then adding 4. Find the number.

Q2 Solve the following:
  a) $2x^2 = 18$ **b)** $2x^2 = 72$ **c)** $3x^2 = 27$ **d)** $4x^2 = 36$ **e)** $5x^2 = 5$

Q3 Solve the following:
  a) $3x + 1 = 2x + 6$ **c)** $5x - 1 = 3x + 19$ **e)** $x + 15 = 4x$
  b) $4x + 3 = 3x + 7$ **d)** $x + 2 = \frac{1}{2}x - 1$ **f)** $3x + 3 = 2x + 12$

Q4 Solve the following:
  a) $3x - 8 = 7$ **d)** $2x - 9 = 25$ **f)** $5x - 2 = 6x - 7$
  b) $2(x - 3) = -2$ **e)** $\frac{24}{x} + 2 = 6$ **g)** $30 - \frac{x^2}{2} = 28$
  c) $4(2x - 1) = 60$

Q5 (x+1) cm   A square has sides of length $(x + 1)$ cm. Find the value of x if:

  a) the perimeter of the square is 66 cm
  b) the perimeter of the square is 152.8 cm.

  With these wordy ones, you just have to write your own equation from the information you're given.

Q6 Mr Smith sent his car to the local garage. He spent £x on new parts, four times this amount on labour and finally £29 for an MOT test. If the total bill was for £106.50, find the value of x.

Q7 Solve:
  a) $2(x - 3) - (x - 2) = 5$ **g)** $\frac{x}{3} + 7 = 12$ **j)** $41 - \frac{x}{11} = 35$
  b) $5(x + 2) - 3(x - 5) = 29$
  c) $2(x + 2) + 3(x + 4) = 31$ **h)** $\frac{x}{10} + 18 = 29$ **k)** $\frac{x}{100} - 3 = 4$
  d) $10(x + 3) - 4(x - 2) = 7(x + 5)$
  e) $5(4x + 3) = 4(7x - 5) + 3(9 - 2x)$ **i)** $17 - \frac{x^2}{3} = 5$ **l)** $\frac{120}{x} = 16$
  f) $3(7 + 2x) + 2(1 - x) = 19$

Q8 Joan, Kate and Linda win £2400 on the National Lottery between them. Joan gets a share of £x, whilst Kate gets twice as much as Joan. Linda's share is £232 less than Joan's amount.
  a) Write down an expression for the amounts Joan, Kate and Linda win.
  b) Write down an equation in terms of x, and solve it.
  c) Write down the amounts Kate and Linda receive.

Q9 All the angles in the diagram are right angles.
  a) Write down an expression for the perimeter of the shape.
  b) Write down an expression for the area of the shape.
  c) For what value of x will the perimeter and area be numerically equal?

Big blobs and broomsticks...

Solving Equations

Q10   Solve the following:

    a) $5(x - 1) + 3(x - 4) = -11$

    b) $3(x + 2) + 2(x - 4) = x - 3(x + 3)$

    c) $\dfrac{3x}{2} + 3 = x$

    d) $3(4x + 2) = 2(2x - 1)$

    e) $\dfrac{5x + 7}{9} = 3$

    f) $\dfrac{2x + 7}{11} = 3$

It's easy — you just put the 2 bits together and there's your equation. Then all you've got to do is solve it...

Q11   For what value of x is the expression $14 - \dfrac{x}{2}$ equal to the value $\dfrac{3x - 4}{2}$?

Q12   Two men are decorating a room. One has painted 20 m² and the other only 6 m². They continue painting and manage to paint another x m² each. If the first man has painted exactly three times the area painted by the second man, find the value of x.

Q13   Carol's father was 24 years old when Carol was born. Now he is four times as old as Carol. How old is Carol?

Q14   Mr Jones is 4 years older than his wife and 31 years older than his son. Their ages add up to 82 years. If Mr Jones is x years old, find the value of x and find the ages of his wife and son.

Q15   Solve the following:

    a) $\dfrac{y}{2} + 2 = 13$

    b) $\dfrac{3x}{4} - 2 = 4$

    c) $\dfrac{2z}{5} - 3 = -5$

    d) $\dfrac{1}{5}(x - 4) = 3$

    e) $\dfrac{2}{3}(x + 1) = 16$

    f) $\dfrac{3}{5}(4x - 3) = 15$

    g) $\dfrac{8}{x^2} = \dfrac{32}{36}$

    h) $\dfrac{12}{5x^2} = \dfrac{3}{20}$

    i) $\dfrac{14}{3x^2} = \dfrac{2}{21}$

Q16   A train travels at 70 mph for x hours and then at 80 mph for $3\frac{3}{4}$ hours. If the train covers 405 miles of track, find the value of x.

Q17   Solve the following:

    a) $\dfrac{4x + 3}{2} + x = \dfrac{5x + 41}{4}$

Remember to do the same to the top and the bottom.

    b) $\dfrac{5}{7}(x - 2) - \dfrac{3}{4}(x + 3) = -4$

Q18   A triangle has lengths as shown below. Find the length of each side, if the length of AC exceeds that of AB by ½ cm.

Rearranging Formulas

Rearranging is getting the letter you want out of the formula and making it the subject. And it's exactly the same method as for solving equations, which can't be bad.

Q1 Rearrange the following formulas to make the letter in brackets the new subject.

a) $g = 10 - 4h$ (h)

b) $d = \frac{1}{2}(c + 4)$ (c)

c) $j = -2(3 - k)$ (k)

d) $a = \frac{2b}{3}$ (b)

e) $f = \frac{3g}{8}$ (g)

f) $y = \frac{x}{2} - 3$ (x)

g) $s = \frac{t}{6} + 10$ (t)

h) $p = 4q^2$ (q)

Q2 Jason is saving up to go travelling next year and has got a temporary job selling cars. He is paid a basic wage of £500 a month, plus a bonus of £50 for each car he sells. He has a spreadsheet to keep track of his money, which calculates his wages (£w) after working for m months and selling c cars, using the following formula:

$$w = 500m + 50c$$

a) Rearrange the formula to make c the subject.

b) Find the number of cars Jason needs to sell in 11 months to earn £12 100.

Q3 The cost of hiring a car is £28 per day plus 25p per mile.

a) Find the cost of hiring the car for a day and travelling:

    i) 40 miles

    ii) 80 miles

b) Write down a formula to give the cost of hiring a car (£c) for one day, and travelling n miles.

c) Rearrange the formula to make n the subject.

d) How many miles can you travel, during one day, if you have a budget of:

    i) £34,   **ii)** £50,   **iii)** £56.50.

Q4 Rearrange the following formulas to make the letter in brackets the new subject.

a) $y = x^2 - 2$ (x)

b) $y = \sqrt{(x + 3)}$ (x)

c) $r = \left(\frac{s}{2}\right)^2$ (s)

d) $f = \frac{10 + g}{3}$ (g)

e) $w = \frac{5 - z}{2}$ (z)

f) $v = \frac{1}{3}x^2 h$ (x)

g) $v^2 = u^2 + 2as$ (a)

h) $v^2 = u^2 + 2as$ (u)

i) $t = 2\pi\sqrt{\dfrac{l}{g}}$ (g)

Q5 Mrs Smith buys x jumpers for £J each and sells them in her shop for a total price of £T.

a) Write down an expression for the amount of money she paid for all the jumpers.

b) Using your answer to **a)**, write down a formula for the profit £P Mrs Smith makes selling all the jumpers.

c) Rearrange the formula to make J the subject.

d) Given that Mrs Smith makes a profit of £156 by selling 13 jumpers for a total of £364 find the price she paid for each jumper originally.

Rearranging Formulas

Q6 A website offering digital photo printing charges 12p per print plus 60p postage.

a) Find the cost of ordering:
   i) 12 prints.
   ii) 24 prints.

b) Write down a formula for the cost C, in pence, of ordering x prints.

c) Rearrange the formula to make x the subject.

d) A regular customer is looking through old receipts to check she has been charged the right amount. How many prints should she have received in each of her last three transactions if she was charged:
   i) £4.92
   ii) £6.36
   iii) £12.12.

Q7 Rearrange the following formulas, by collecting terms in x and looking for common factors, to make x the new subject.

a) $xy = z - 2x$

b) $ax = 3x + b$

c) $4x - y = xz$

d) $xy = 3z - 5x + y$

e) $xy = xz - 2$

f) $2(x - y) = z(x + 3)$

g) $xyz = x - y - wz$

h) $3y(x + z) = y(2z - x)$

Q8 Rearrange the following to make the letter in brackets the new subject.

a) $pq = 3p + 4r - 2q$ (p)

b) $fg + 2e = 5 - 2g$ (g)

c) $a(b - 2) = c(b + 3)$ (b)

d) $pq^2 = rq^2 + 4$ (q)

e) $4(a - b) + c(a - 2) = ad$ (a)

f) $\dfrac{x^2}{3} - y = x^2$ (x)

g) $\sqrt{hk^2 - 14} = k$ (k)

h) $2\sqrt{x} + y = z\sqrt{x} + 4$ (x)

i) $\dfrac{a}{b} = \dfrac{1}{3}(b - a)$ (a)

j) $\dfrac{m + n}{m - n} = \dfrac{3}{4}$ (m)

k) $\sqrt{\dfrac{(d - e)}{e}} = 7$ (e)

l) $\dfrac{x - 2y}{xy} = 3$ (y)

These are getting quite tricky — you've got to <u>collect like terms</u>, before you can make anything else the subject.

Q9 Rearrange the following formulas to make y the new subject.

a) $x(y - 1) = y$

b) $x(y + 2) = y - 3$

c) $x = \dfrac{y^2 + 1}{2y^2 - 1}$

d) $x = \dfrac{2y^2 + 1}{3y^2 - 2}$

Factorising Quadratics

Q1 Factorise the quadratics first, and then solve the equations:

a) $x^2 + 3x - 10 = 0$

b) $x^2 - 5x + 6 = 0$

c) $x^2 - 2x + 1 = 0$

d) $x^2 - 4x + 3 = 0$

e) $x^2 - x - 20 = 0$

f) $x^2 - 4x - 5 = 0$

g) $x^2 + 6x - 7 = 0$

h) $x^2 + 14x + 49 = 0$

i) $x^2 - 2x - 15 = 0$.

Q2 Rearrange into the form "$x^2 + bx + c = 0$", then solve by factorising:

a) $x^2 + 6x = 16$

b) $x^2 + 5x = 36$

c) $x^2 + 4x = 45$

d) $x^2 = 5x$

e) $x^2 = 11x$

f) $x^2 - 21 = 4x$

g) $x^2 - 300 = 20x$

h) $x^2 + 48 = 26x$

i) $x^2 + 36 = 13x$

j) $x + 5 - \dfrac{14}{x} = 0$

k) $x + 4 - \dfrac{21}{x} = 0$

l) $x(x - 3) = 10$

m) $x^2 - 3(x + 6) = 0$

n) $x - \dfrac{63}{x} = 2$

o) $x + 1 - \dfrac{12}{x}$

Q3 Solve $x^2 - \dfrac{1}{4} = 0$.

Q4 The area of a rectangular swimming pool is 28 m². The width is x m. The difference between the length and width is 3 m. Find the value of x.

x m

Q5 A rug has length x m. The width is exactly 1 m less than the length.

x m

a) Write down an expression for the area of the rug.

b) If the area of the rug is 6 m², find the value of x.

Q6 A triangle has height $(x + 1)$ cm and a base of $2x$ cm.

a) Write down an expression for the area of the triangle and simplify it.

b) If the area of the triangle is 12 cm², find the value of x.

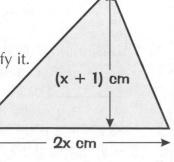
(x + 1) cm

2x cm

Q7 A square room has a floor of sides x metres. The height of the walls is 3 m. Write down an expression for:

a) the floor area

b) the area of all four walls.

c) If the total area of the floor and the four walls is 64 m², form a quadratic equation and solve it to find x.

Completing the Square

All you're doing is writing it in the form "$(x + 4)^2 + 2$" instead of "$x^2 + 8x + 18$" — don't let the name put you off.

Q1 Complete the square for the following expressions:

a) $x^2 - 4x - 5$
b) $x^2 - 2x + 1$
c) $x^2 + x + 1$
d) $x^2 - 6x + 9$
e) $x^2 - 6x + 7$
f) $x^2 - 4x$

First look at what you need to put in the bracket to get the x^2 and x terms. Then work the number part out at the end.

g) $x^2 + 3x - 4$
h) $x^2 - x - 3$
i) $x^2 - 10x + 25$
j) $x^2 - 10x$
k) $x^2 + 8x + 17$
l) $x^2 - 12x + 35$

Q2 Solve the following quadratic equations by completing the square. Write down your answers to no more than 2 d.p.

a) $x^2 + 3x - 1 = 0$
b) $x^2 - x - 3 = 0$
c) $x^2 + 4x - 3 = 0$
d) $x^2 + x - 1 = 0$

e) $x^2 - 3x - 5 = 0$
f) $2x^2 - 6x + 1 = 0$
g) $3x^2 - 3x - 2 = 0$
h) $3x^2 - 6x - 1 = 0$

It's quite a cunning method, really... but I admit it takes a bit of getting used to — make sure you've learnt all the steps, then it's just practice, practice...

Algebra Crossword

ACROSS

1) Put brackets in (9)
4) You could do this to an equation (5)
6) You often do 1) across to this type of equation (9)
9) When two things are the same they are _____ (5)
10) Complete this shape (6)

You might need to finish Unit 2 before you can complete some of these clues.

Think of this as a treat you can come back to.

DOWN

1) You should rearrange these (8)
2) $x \leqslant -6$ is an example of an _____ (10)
3) $2x + 4 = 6$ is one (8)
5) Something you collect when simplifying. Like _____ (5)
7) Equations that are true for all values of their variables (10)
8) These are found a lot in algebra (and post boxes) (7)

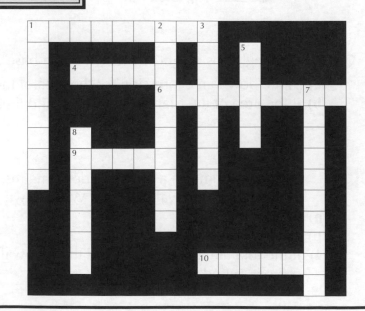

Simultaneous Equations

To solve simultaneous equations from scratch, you've got to get rid of either x or y first — to leave you with an equation with just one unknown in it.

Q1 Use the linear equation (the one with no x^2s in it) to find an expression for y. Then substitute it into the quadratic equation (the one <u>with</u> x^2s in it), to solve these equations:

a) $y = x^2 + 2$
$y = x + 14$

b) $y = x^2 - 8$
$y = 3x + 10$

c) $y = 2x^2$
$y = x + 3$

d) $x + 5y = 30$
$x^2 + \frac{4}{5}x = y$

e) $y = 1 - 13x$
$y = 4x^2 + 4$

f) $y = 3(x^2 + 3)$
$14x + y = 1$

Q2 Solve the following simultaneous equations:

a) $4x + 6y = 16$
$x + 2y = 5$

b) $3x + 8y = 24$
$x + y = 3$

c) $3y - 8x = 24$
$3y + 2x = 9$

Careful with parts d) to f) — some of them are quadratics...

d) $y = x^2 - 2$
$y = 3x + 8$

e) $y = 3x^2 - 10$
$13x - y = 14$

f) $y + 2 = 2x^2$
$y + 3x = 0$

g) $3y - 10x - 17 = 0$
$\frac{1}{3}y + 2x - 5 = 0$

h) $\frac{x}{2} - 2y = 5$
$12y + x - 2 = 0$

i) $x + y = \frac{1}{2}(y - x)$
$x + y = 2$

Q3 Two farmers are buying livestock at a market. Farmer Ed buys 6 sheep and 5 pigs for £430 and Farmer Jacob buys 4 sheep and 10 pigs for £500.

a) If sheep cost £x and pigs cost £y, write down the two purchases as a pair of simultaneous equations.

b) Solve for x and y.

Q4 On Farmer Palmer's farm, the cats have got into the chicken coop and are causing chaos. Falmer Palmer counts, in total, 11 heads and 30 legs. How many cats and how many chickens are in the chicken coop?

Q5 Isobel is buying pick & mix sweets. She weighs out 20 jellies and 30 toffees which come to 230 g. She takes one of each off the scales before they get bagged up, and the weight drops to 221 g. How much does an individual toffee weigh?

Q6 Find the value of x and y for each of the following rectangles, by first writing down a pair of simultaneous equations and then solving them.

Q7 Two customers enter a shop to buy milk and cornflakes. Mrs Smith buys 5 pints of milk and 2 boxes of cornflakes and spends £3.44. Mr Brown buys 4 pints of milk and 3 boxes of cornflakes and receives £6.03 change after paying with a £10 note. Write down a pair of simultaneous equations and solve them to find the price in pence of a pint of milk (m) and a box of cornflakes (c).

Q8 Solve $\dfrac{3(x - y)}{5} = x - 3y = x - 6$.

Number Sequences

Q1 For each of the sequences below, write down the next three numbers and the rule that you used.

a) 1, 3, 5, 7,...

b) 2, 4, 8, 16,...

c) 3, 30, 300, 3000,...

d) 3, 7, 11, 15,...

e) 19, 14, 9, 4, –1,...

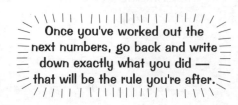

Once you've worked out the next numbers, go back and write down exactly what you did — that will be the rule you're after.

Q2 For the following, use the rule given to generate the first 5 terms of the sequence.

a) $3n + 1$, when $n = 1, 2, 3, 4$ and 5.

b) $5n - 2$, when $n = 1, 2, 3, 4$ and 5.

c) n^2, when $n = 1, 2, 3, 4,$ and 5.

d) $n^2 - 3$, when $n = 1, 2, 3, 4,$ and 5.

Q3 Write down an expression for the nth term of the following sequences:

a) 2, 4, 6, 8, …

b) 1, 3, 5, 7, …

c) 5, 10, 15, 20, …

d) 5, 8, 11, 14, …

Q4 In the following sequences, write down the next 3 terms and the nth term:

a) 7, 10, 13, 16,...

b) 12, 17, 22, 27,...

c) 6, 16, 26, 36,...

d) 54, 61, 68, 75,...

X and Y Coordinates

Q1 ABCD is a <u>parallelogram</u>. A is (-1, 3), B is (-2,-1) and C is (4,-1).
Draw axes with *x* from -3 to 5 and *y* from -2 to 4.
Plot A, B and C then find the <u>missing coordinates</u> for D.

Q2 Draw axes with *x* from -9 to 9 and *y* from -12 to 12.
On the <u>same</u> set of axes draw the following shapes and find their
<u>missing pair of coordinates</u>.

a) ABCD is a <u>square</u>
A is (1, 1)
B is ?
C is (-3,-3)
D is (-3, 1)

c) ABCD is a <u>rectangle</u>
A is ?
B is (3,-8)
C is (3,-6)
D is (-5,-6)

e) ABCD is a <u>parallelogram</u>
A is (-2,-10)
B is (4,-10)
C is (6,-12)
D is ?

b) ABCD is a <u>parallelogram</u>
A is (2, 8)
B is (6, 8)
C is ?
D is (1, 5)

d) ABCD is a <u>kite</u>
A is (-9, 3)
B is (-6, 8)
C is (-4, 8)
D is ?

f) ABCD is a <u>parallelogram</u>
A is (-8, 10)
B is (-6, 10)
C is ?
D is (-5, 12)

Q3 ABCD is a <u>rectangle</u> with the line $x = 0$
as a <u>line of symmetry</u>.
Draw axes with *x* from -3 to 3 and
y from -3 to 3.
If A = (-2,-2) and B is (-2, 1), find the
<u>coordinates of C and D</u>.

I'm afraid you'll just have to get the hang of using things like "the line x = 4", as they seem to prefer it to "a vertical line through the point 4 on the horizontal axis". Yeah, that is a bit long winded, I guess — so maybe they've got a point...

Straight Line Graphs

Q1 Which letters represent the following lines:

a) $x = y$
b) $x = 5$
c) $y = -x$
d) $x = 0$
e) $y = -7$
f) $x + y = 0$
g) $y = 5$
h) $x - y = 0$
i) $y = 0$
j) $x = -7$?

Don't get confused if you've got "x + y = ... " — just rearrange the equation to "y = -x + ..." and as if by magic, you've got a line you recognise.

Q2 Complete the following table for the line $y = 3x - 1$:

x	-4	-3	-2	-1	0	1	2	3	4
3x									
-1									
y									

Plot these points on graph paper and hence draw the graph of $y = 3x - 1$.
Use a scale of 1 cm for 2 units on the y-axis and 2 cm for 1 unit on the x-axis.

Q3 Complete the following table for the line $y = \frac{1}{2}x - 3$:

x	-6	-4	-2	0	2	4	6
½ x							
-3							
y							

Plot these points on graph paper and hence draw the graph of $y = \frac{1}{2}x - 3$.

Straight Line Graphs

If you know it's a straight line, you only really need <u>two</u> points, but it's always a <u>good idea</u> to plot three — it's a bit of a safety net, really.

Q4 Complete this table of values for $y = 2x + 3$:

X	0	3	8
y			

Plot these points on graph paper and draw the graph of $y = 2x + 3$.
Use your graph to find:

a) The value of y when $x = 5$
b) The value of y when $x = 2$
c) The value of x when $y = 11$
d) The value of x when $y = 17$

Q5 Complete this table of values for $y = \frac{1}{4}x - 3$:

X	-8	-4	8
y			

Plot these points on graph paper and draw the graph of $y = \frac{1}{4}x - 3$.
Use your graph to find:

a) The value of y when $x = 4$
b) The value of y when $x = 0$
c) The value of x when $y = -2$
d) The value of x when $y = -1.5$

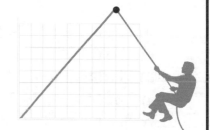

Q6 The cost of electricity is calculated using the formula:
Total cost = Fixed charge + (cost per unit × number of units).
Customers can choose two different methods of payment:
Method A: Fixed charge £10, cost per unit 25p
Method B: Fixed charge £40, cost per unit 5p
Copy and complete this table:

Number of Units used	0	100	200	300
Cost using method A				
Cost using method B				

Plot these points on a graph (put the number of units on the horizontal axis, cost on the vertical axis):

a) Use your graph to find the total cost when 70 units are used for:
  i) Method A
  ii) Method B

b) Miss Wright used 75 units. Which method should she use to minimize her bill, Method A or Method B?

c) Use your graph to work out how many units Miss Wright would have to use for both methods to cost the same amount.

y = mx + c

Writing the equation of a line in the form y = mx + c gives you a nifty way of finding the gradient and y-intercept. Remember that — it'll save you loads of time. Anything for an easy life...

Q1 For each of the following lines, give the gradient and the coordinates of the point where the line cuts the *y*-axis.

a) $y = 4x + 3$

b) $y = 3x - 2$

c) $y = 2x + 1$

d) $y = -3x + 3$

e) $y = 5x$

f) $y = -2x + 3$

g) $y = -6x - 4$

h) $y = x$

i) $y = -\frac{1}{2}x + 3$

j) $y = \frac{1}{4}x + 2$

k) $3y = 4x + 6$

l) $2y = -5x - 4$

m) $8y = 4x - 12$

n) $3y = 7x + 5$

o) $x + y = 0$

p) $x - y = 0$

q) $y - x = 3$

r) $x - 3 = y$

s) $y - 7 = 3x$

t) $y - 5x = 3$

u) $y + 2x + 3 = 0$

v) $y - 2x - 4 = 0$

I know these are a bit algebra-ish, but don't worry, they won't bite.

Q2 What is the gradient of:
a) line A
b) line B
c) line C
d) line D
e) line E
f) line F
g) line G
h) line H
i) line I
j) line J
k) a line parallel to A
l) a line parallel to B
m) a line perpendicular to C?

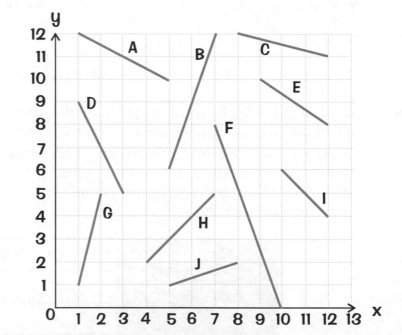

Uphill gradients are always positive, downhill always negative. Impressed? Hmmm....thought not. Can be a bit of an uphill battle, these.

Q3 What is the gradient of the lines joining the points:
a) (3, 5) and (5, 9)
b) (6, 3) and (10, 5)
c) (-6, 4) and (-3, 1)
d) (8, 2) and (4, 10)
e) (8, 5) and (6, 4)
f) (-3, -1) and (1, -4)?

Q4 Lauren works in a ski resort grading ski runs. A blue run has a gradient shallower than -0.2, a red is steeper than a blue, but has a gradient shallower than -0.25. Anything steeper is a black.
A run covers a horizontal distance of 1.75 km long and descends 400 meters.
What colour should Lauren grade it?

y = mx + c

Q5   Find the equations of the following lines:

a) A
b) B
c) C
d) D
e) E
f) F

Yeah, OK, this sounds a bit scary, but just work out the gradient (m) and look at the y-intercept (c) and pop them back into "y = mx + c"... easy lemons.

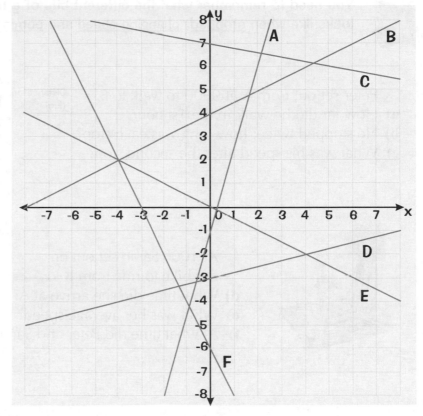

Q6   Find the equation of the straight line which passes through:

a) (3, 7) and has a gradient of 1
b) (2, 8) and has a gradient of 3
c) (4, –4) and has a gradient of –1
d) (–1, 7) and has a gradient of –3

Q7   Write down the equation of the line which passes through the points:

a) (2, 2) and (5, 5)
b) (1, 3) and (4, 12)
c) (–2, –3) and (5, 11)

Here's a bit more practice with those gradients. Thought you'd like that.

Q8   Plot graphs of the straight lines with the following gradients and y-intercepts:

a) m = 2, c = -1
b) m = ½ and c = 5
c) m = -3 and c = 2.5

Q9   What is the value of x or y if:

a) the point $(x, 13)$ is on the line $y = 3x + 1$
b) the point $(x, –2)$ is on the line $y = \frac{1}{2}x – 6$
c) the point $(4, y)$ is on the line $y = 2x – 1$
d) the point $(–3, y)$ is on the line $y = –3x$?

Q10   Which of the following points lie on the line $y = 3x – 1$?
(7, 20), (6, 15), (5, 14)

D/T and V/T Graphs

You need to remember what the different bits of a travel graph mean — what it looks like when <u>stopped</u>, <u>changing speed</u> and <u>coming back</u> to the starting point.

Q1   Peter set out from A at 0900 to walk to B.
   a) How far did he walk in the 1st hour?
   b) He stopped twice; how long was each stop?
   c) What was his speed after the second stop?

At 1000 Sarah set out on her bike to ride from B to A.
   d) What time did she arrive at A?
   e) What was her average speed?
   f) At what time did Peter and Sarah pass each other?

Q2   Dave drives a bus from Kendal to Ingleton and back again. The bus company graphed the journey to help them organise their bus schedules.

   a) How long did it take to get to Ingleton?
   b) How much time was spent driving to and from Ingleton excluding stops?
   c) What was the average speed for the journey from Kendal to Ingleton?
   d) What was Dave's fastest speed?
   e) The transport manager wants Dave to reduce the duration of the stops on the Kendal to Ingleton route so that he can make another journey from Kendal to Windermere starting at 1630. Would this be possible?

Q3   Mr. Smith leaves home at 0730 to go to work. He walks at a steady 6 km/h for 2 km. He catches the 0755 train which takes 35 mins to travel 50 km. He then walks 3 km to work and arrives at 0900.

   Draw a graph to show this.
   How long did he wait at the station for the train?

D/T and V/T Graphs

Q4 A train operator plans to purchase a new engine. They've graphed the journeys made by five engines over a 100 km stretch of track to help them decide which one is best.

a) Calculate the speed of each train and state which one was the fastest.

b) How could you tell by looking at the diagram which was the fastest and which was the slowest?

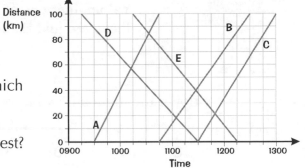

Q5 On sports day the first three in the 1000 m race ran as shown in the graph below.

a) Which runner, A, B or C, won the race?

b) How long did the winner take?

c) Which runner kept up a steady speed?

d) What was that speed
   i) in m/min?
   ii) km/h?

e) Which runner achieved the fastest speed and what was that speed?

Q6 Two cars start a journey at midday (1200) — one travels from town A to village B, and the other from village B to town A. A and B are 80 km apart. The car from town A travels at an average speed of 48 km/h and the other car, from village B, at 60 km/h.

a) Draw a graph to show these journeys.

b) At what time do the cars pass? (approx.)

c) How far from A are they when they pass?

> Use the speeds given to work out the time it takes for each car to travel the 80 km.

Q7 A girl set off on an all-day walk. She started at 0915 and walked at a steady speed for 9 km before stopping at 1100 for a 20 min break. She then set off again at a steady speed and walked 8 km, stopping at 1300 for 45 mins. After lunch she walked at 3½ km/h for 2½ hrs to her destination.

a) Draw a graph to show this walk.

b) How far did she walk altogether?

c) What was the average speed for the whole walk?

d) What was her fastest walking speed?

Inequalities

 Yet another one of those bits of Maths that looks worse than it is — these are just like equations, really, except for the symbols.

Q1 Write down the inequality represented by each diagram below.

a)

b)

c)

d)

e)

f)

g)

h)

Q2 By drawing an appropriate part of the number line for each question, represent each of the following inequalities.

a) $x > 5$ **c)** $2 > x > -5$ **e)** $3 \geq x > -2$ **g)** $-3 \leq x \leq -2$
b) $x \leq 2$ **d)** $3 > x \geq -2$ **f)** $7 \geq x > 6$ **h)** $0 \geq x > -3$

Q3 Draw and label a number line from –5 to 5 for each of the following questions. Represent the inequalities on your number lines.

a) $x^2 \leq 4$ **c)** $x^2 \leq 9$ **e)** $16 \geq x^2$ **g)** $9 > x^2$
b) $x^2 < 1$ **d)** $25 \geq x^2$ **f)** $x^2 \leq 1$ **h)** $x^2 \leq 0$

Q4 Solve the following:
a) $3x + 2 > 11$ **e)** $2x - 7 \geq 8$ **i)** $5(x + 2) \geq 25$ **m)** $8 - 3x \geq 14$
b) $5x + 4 < 24$ **f)** $17 + 4x < 33$ **j)** $4(x - 1) > 40$ **n)** $16 - x < 11$
c) $5x + 7 \leq 32$ **g)** $2(x + 3) < 20$ **k)** $10 - 2x > 4x - 8$ **o)** $16 - x > 1$
d) $3x + 12 \leq 30$ **h)** $2(5x - 4) < 32$ **l)** $7 - 2x \leq 4x + 10$ **p)** $12 - 3x \leq 18$

Inequalities

Q5   Find the largest integer x, such that $2x + 5 \geq 5x - 2$.

Q6   When a number is subtracted from 11, and this new number is then divided by two, the result is always less than five. Write this information as an inequality and solve it to show the possible values of the number.

Q7   Two schools are merging and a new school is being built to accommodate all the pupils. There will be 1,130 pupils in total in the new school. No class must have more than 32 pupils. How many classrooms are needed?
Show this information as an inequality.

Call the number of classrooms x.

Q8   A couple are planning their wedding. For the reception in a local hotel, they have a budget of £900. If the hotel charges £18 per head, how many guests could be invited? Show this information as an inequality.

Q9   The shaded region satisfies three inequalities. Write down these inequalities.

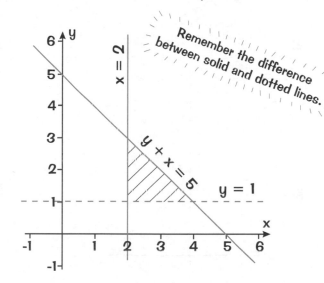

Remember the difference between solid and dotted lines.

Q10   Draw a set of axes with the x-axis from –2 to 6 and the y-axis from –1 to 7. Show on a graph the region enclosed by the following three inequalities.

$$y < 6, \qquad x + y \geq 5 \qquad \text{and} \qquad x \leq 5$$

Q11   Draw a set of axes with the x-axis from –4 to 5 and the y-axis from –3 to 6. Show on a graph the region enclosed by the following.

$$y \leq 2x + 4, \qquad y < 5 - x \qquad \text{and} \qquad y \geq \frac{x}{3} - 1$$

Q12   A company are recruiting new members of staff. All applicants must take two online tests. To get an interview, applicants must score higher than 5 on the first test, at least 7 on the second, and have a total combined score of at least 14.

   a) Write out three inequalities to represent the three criteria for getting an interview. Use x for the score on the first test and y for the score on the second test.

   b) The company want to analyse the quality of applicants by plotting their test scores on a graph, and picking out the ones who satisfy the criteria. Using suitable axes, show on a graph the region enclosed by the three inequalities where suitable candidates would be placed.

Graphs to Recognise

Q1 Identify the type of graph shown below.
Choose from straight line, quadratic, cubic and reciprocal:

a)

b)

c)

d)

e)

f)

g)

h)

i)

j)

k)

l)

Graphs to Recognise

Q2   Here are some equations, and there are some curves below. Match the equations to the curves on this page and the following page.

a) $y = 3x + 1$ **g)** $y = -x^2$ **m)** $y = x^3 + 3$ **s)** $y = \dfrac{2}{x}$

b) $y = 4x - 1$ **h)** $y = x^2 + 2$ **n)** $y = 2x^3 - 3$ **t)** $y = \dfrac{1}{x^2}$

c) $y = -2x - 1$ **i)** $y = x^2 - 3$ **o)** $y = -\dfrac{1}{2}x^3 + 2$ **u)** $y = -\dfrac{1}{x^2}$

d) $y = -3x + 2$ **j)** $y = -x^2 + 3$ **p)** $y = -x^3 + 3$

e) $y = -2x$ **k)** $y = -x^2 - 3$ **q)** $y = x^3$

f) $y = 3x$ **l)** $y = x^2$ **r)** $y = -\dfrac{3}{x}$

i)

ii)

iii)

iv)

v)

vi)

vii)

viii)

ix)

You'll need to be able to <u>sketch a graph</u> from <u>memory</u> — yeah, scary huh.
Don't worry — they only expect you to remember the <u>4 main ones</u> (phew) —
<u>straight line</u> (easy), x² (buckets), x³ (wiggly) and 1/x (2 bits and "x=0" missing).

Graphs to Recognise

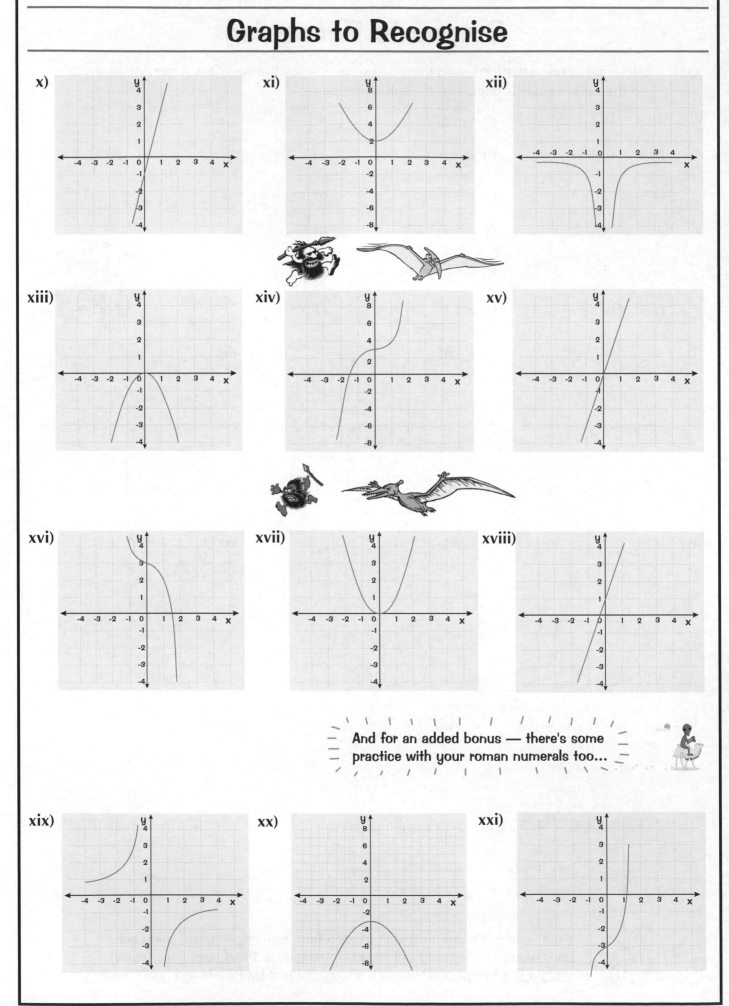

x)

xi)

xii)

xiii)

xiv)

xv)

xvi)

xvii)

xviii)

And for an added bonus — there's some practice with your roman numerals too...

xix)

xx)

xxi)

Quadratic Graphs

So, you can spot a quadratic graph at ten paces, but can you draw one...

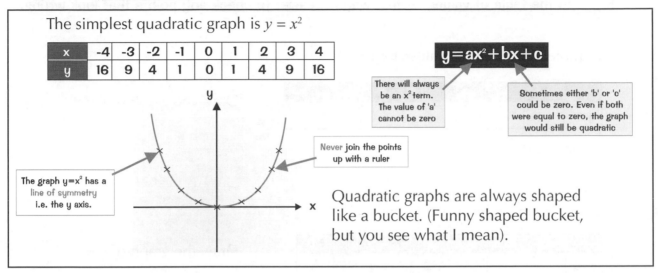

The simplest quadratic graph is $y = x^2$

x	-4	-3	-2	-1	0	1	2	3	4
y	16	9	4	1	0	1	4	9	16

$y = ax^2 + bx + c$

There will always be an x^2 term. The value of 'a' cannot be zero

Sometimes either 'b' or 'c' could be zero. Even if both were equal to zero, the graph would still be quadratic

Never join the points up with a ruler

The graph $y = x^2$ has a line of symmetry i.e. the y axis.

Quadratic graphs are always shaped like a bucket. (Funny shaped bucket, but you see what I mean).

Q1 Complete this <u>table of values</u> for the quadratic graph $y = 2x^2$.

a) Draw axes with x from -4 to 4 and y from 0 to 32.

b) Plot these 9 points and join them with a <u>smooth curve</u>.

c) Label your graph.

x	-4	-3	-2	-1	0	1	2	3	4
$y = 2x^2$	32	18					8		

Remember to square first then × 2

Q2 Complete this table of values for the graph $y = x^2 + x$.

x	-4	-3	-2	-1	0	1	2	3	4
x^2	16	9				4			
$y = x^2 + x$	12					2			

By putting more steps in your table of values, the arithmetic is easier

a) Draw axes with x from -4 to 4 and y from 0 to 20.

b) Plot the points and join them with a smooth curve.

c) Draw and label the <u>line of symmetry</u> for the quadratic graph $y = x^2 + x$.

If the x^2 term has a <u>minus</u> sign in front of it, the bucket will be turned <u>upside down</u>.

Q3 a) Complete this table of values for the graph $y = 3 - x^2$.

b) Draw the graph $y = 3 - x^2$ for x from -4 to 4.

c) State the <u>maximum value</u> of the graph $y = 3 - x^2$.

x	-4	-3	-2	-1	0	1	2	3	4
3	3	3	3	3	3	3	3	3	3
$-x^2$	-16						-4		
$y = 3 - x^2$	-13						-1		

Cubic Graphs

You go about a cubic in the same way as you would a quadratic — but you should get a different shaped graph, of course. It's always a good idea to put <u>lots of steps</u> in the <u>table of values</u> — that way it's <u>easier to check</u> any points that look wrong.

Q1 Complete this table of values for $y = x^3$:

x	-3	-2	-1	0	1	2	3
y=x³							

Draw the graph of $y = x^3$.

Q2 Complete this table of values for $y = -x^3$:

x	-3	-2	-1	0	1	2	3
y=-x³							

Draw the graph of $y = -x^3$.

Q3 Complete this table of values for $y = x^3 + 4$:

x	-3	-2	-1	0	1	2	3
x³							
+4							
y							

Draw the graph of $y = x^3 + 4$.

Remember — no rulers.

Q4 Complete this table of values for $y = -x^3 - 4$:

x	-3	-2	-1	0	1	2	3
-x³							
-4							
y							

Draw the graph of $y = -x^3 - 4$.

Q5 Look at your graphs for questions 1 and 3. What has been done to graph 1 to change it into graph 3? Without plotting a table of values draw the graph of $y = x^3 - 4$.

Q6 Look at your graphs for questions 2 and 4. What has been done to graph 2 to change it into graph 4? Without plotting a table of values draw the graph of $y = -x^3 + 4$.

Simultaneous Equations and Graphs

Q1 Solve the following simultaneous equations by drawing graphs. Use values $0 \leqslant x \leqslant 6$

a) $y = x$
   $y = 9 - 2x$

b) $y = 2x + 1$
   $2y = 8 + x$

c) $y = 4 - 2x$
   $x + y = 3$

d) $y = 3 - x$
   $3x + y = 5$

e) $2x + y = 6$
   $y = 3x + 1$

f) $y = 2x$
   $y = x + 1$

g) $x + y = 5$
   $2x - 1 = y$

h) $2y = 3x$
   $y = x + 1$

i) $y = x - 3$
   $y + x = 7$

j) $y = x + 1$
   $2x + y = 10$

Q2 The diagram shows the graphs:
   $y = x^2 - x$
   $y = x + 2$
   $y = 8$
   $y = -2x + 4$

Use the graphs to find the solutions to:

a) $x^2 - x = 0$

b) $x^2 - x = x + 2$

c) $x^2 - x = 8$

d) $x^2 - x = -2x + 4$

e) $-2x + 4 = x + 2$

f) $x^2 - x - 8 = 0$

g) $x^2 + x = 4$

 These equations look a bit nasty, but they're just made up of the equations you've got graphs for. And you know how to do the rest of it, don't you...

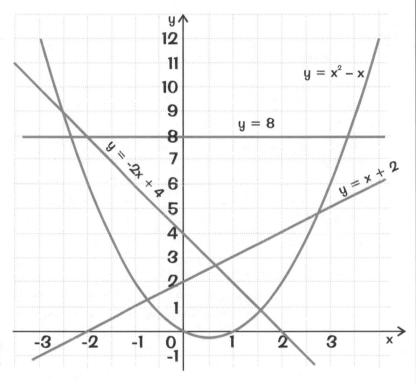

Q3 Complete this table for $y = -\frac{1}{2}x^2 + 5$:

X	-4	-3	-2	-1	0	1	2	3	4
-½ x²									
+5									
y									

Draw the graph $y = -\frac{1}{2}x^2 + 5$.
Use your graph to solve the following equations (to 1 d.p.):

a) $-\frac{1}{2}x^2 + 5 = 0$ b) $-\frac{1}{2}x^2 + 5 = -3$ c) $-\frac{1}{2}x^2 + 5 = x$

UNIT 3 — GEOMETRY AND ALGEBRA

The Quadratic Formula

Q1 Find the two values, to 2 d.p, given by each of the following expressions:

a) $\dfrac{2 \pm \sqrt{3}}{2}$

b) $\dfrac{4 \pm \sqrt{10}}{3}$

c) $\dfrac{-2 \pm \sqrt{27}}{2}$

d) $\dfrac{-3 \pm \sqrt{42}}{3}$

e) $\dfrac{-10 \pm \sqrt{160}}{5}$

f) $\dfrac{-27 \pm \sqrt{10}}{2}$

g) $\dfrac{-8 \pm \sqrt{9.5}}{2.4}$

h) $\dfrac{10 \pm \sqrt{88.4}}{23.2}$

Q2 The following quadratics can be solved by factorisation, but practise using the formula to solve them.

a) $x^2 + 8x + 12 = 0$
b) $6x^2 - x - 2 = 0$
c) $x^2 - x - 6 = 0$
d) $x^2 - 3x + 2 = 0$
e) $4x^2 - 15x + 9 = 0$
f) $x^2 - 3x = 0$
g) $36x^2 - 48x + 16 = 0$
h) $3x^2 + 8x = 0$
i) $2x^2 - 7x - 4 = 0$

j) $x^2 + x - 20 = 0$
k) $4x^2 + 8x - 12 = 0$
l) $3x^2 - 11x - 20 = 0$
m) $x + 3 = 2x^2$
n) $5 - 3x - 2x^2 = 0$
o) $1 - 5x + 6x^2 = 0$
p) $3(x^2 + 2x) = 9$
q) $x^2 + 4(x - 3) = 0$
r) $x^2 = 2(4 - x)$

Step number 1...
Write out the formula.

Step number 2...
Write down values
for a, b and c.

Step number 3... sub a, b and c into the formula. Make sure
you divide the <u>whole</u> of the top line by <u>2a</u> — not just ½ of it.

Q3 Solve the following quadratics using the formula. Give your answers to no more than two decimal places.

a) $x^2 + 3x - 1 = 0$
b) $x^2 - 2x - 6 = 0$
c) $x^2 + x - 1 = 0$
d) $x^2 + 6x + 3 = 0$
e) $x^2 + 5x + 2 = 0$
f) $x^2 - x - 1 = 0$
g) $3x^2 + 10x - 8 = 0$

h) $x^2 + 4x + 2 = 0$
i) $x^2 - 6x - 8 = 0$
j) $x^2 - 14x + 11 = 0$
k) $x^2 + 3x - 5 = 0$
l) $7x^2 - 15x + 6 = 0$
m) $2x^2 + 6x - 3 = 0$
n) $2x^2 - 7x + 4 = 0$

Oops, forgot to mention step number 4...
check your answers by putting them <u>back in the equation.</u>

The Quadratic Formula

Q4 Rearrange the following in the form "$ax^2 + bx + c = 0$" and then solve using the quadratic formula. Give your answers to two decimal places.

a) $x^2 = 8 - 3x$

b) $(x + 2)^2 - 3 = 0$

c) $3x(x - 1) = 5$

d) $2x(x + 4) = 1$

e) $x^2 = 4(x + 1)$

f) $(2x - 1)^2 = 5$

g) $3x^2 + 2x = 6$

h) $(x + 2)(x + 3) = 5$

i) $(x - 2)(2x - 1) = 3$

j) $2x + \dfrac{4}{x} = 7$

k) $\left(x - \dfrac{1}{2}\right)^2 = \dfrac{1}{4}$

l) $4x(x - 2) = -3$

 Pythagoras... remember him — you know, that bloke who didn't like angles.

Q5 The sides of a right angled triangle are as shown. Use Pythagoras' theorem to form a quadratic equation in x and then solve it to find x.

2x cm, (2x + 2.4) cm, (x + 3) cm

Q6 The area of a rectangle with length $(x + 4.6)$ cm and width $(x - 2.1)$ cm is 134.63 cm².

a) Form a quadratic equation and solve it to find x to two decimal places.
b) What is the rectangle's perimeter to one decimal place?

(x − 2.1) cm, (x + 4.6) cm

Trial and Improvement

Q1 The cubic equation $x^3 + x = 24$ has a solution between 2 and 3.
Copy the table below and use it to find this solution to 1 d.p.

Guess (x)	Value of $x^3 + x$	Too large or Too small
2	$2^3 + 2 =$	
3	$3^3 + 3 =$	

Q2 The cubic equation $x^3 + x^2 - 4x = 3$ has three solutions. The first solution lies between −3 and −2. The second lies between −1 and 0. The third solution lies between 1 and 2.
Copy the table below and use it to find all three solutions.

Guess (x)	Value of $x^3 + x^2 - 4x$	Too large or Too small
−3	$(-3)^3 + (-3)^2 - 4(-3) = -6$	
−2	$(-2)^3 + (-2)^2 - 4(-2) =$	
−1	$(-1)^3 + (-1)^2 - 4(-1) =$	
0	$(0)^3 + (0)^2 - 4(0) =$	
1	$(1)^3 + (1)^2 - 4(1) =$	
2	$(2)^3 + (2)^2 - 4(2) =$	

The first solution is

.... to 1d.p.

The second solution is

.... to 1d.p.

The third solution is

.... to 1d.p.

Q3 For a craft project, Steph is making some simple boxes.
She cuts out squares of side length x cm from square pieces of card measuring 20 cm by 20 cm, then folds up the sides, as shown. The volume of the boxes (V) can be calculated using the cubic equation:
$$4x^3 - 80x^2 + 400x = V.$$

Use trial and improvement to find the value of x she must use to give the biggest volume of box possible, giving the answer to 1 d.p. The solution lies between 3 cm and 4 cm.

They don't always give you the starting numbers — so if they don't, make sure you pick two opposite cases (one too big, one too small), or you've blown it.

UNIT 3 — GEOMETRY AND ALGEBRA

Direct and Inverse Proportion

Q1   If 17 textbooks cost £150.45, how much will 28 cost?

Q2   If it takes 4 people 28 hours to complete a task, how long would it take just one person?

Q3   A person earns £6.20 an hour. How much do they earn for 15½ hours work?

Q4   On a map, 2 cm represents 3 km.
   a) If two towns are 14 km apart, what is the distance between them on the map?
   b) If two road junctions are 20.3 cm apart on the map, what is their real distance apart?

Q5 y is directly proportional to x. If $y = 5$ when x is 25, find y when x is 100.

Q6 y is directly proportional to x. If y is 1.2 when x is 2.5, find the value of y when $x = 3.75$.

Q7   If $y \propto x$ and $y = 132$ when $x = 10$, find the value of y when $x = 14$.

Q8   If $y \propto x$ and $y = 117$ when $x = 45$, find the value of x when $y = 195$.

Q9   Complete the following tables of values where y is always directly proportional to x.

a)

X	2	4	6
y	5	10	

b)

X	3	6	9
y		9	

c)

X	27		
y	5	10	15

Q10   If $y = 3$ when $x = 8$ and y is inversely proportional to x, find the value of y when $x = 12$.

Direct and Inverse Proportion

Q11 If $y \propto \dfrac{1}{x}$ and $x = 4$ when $y = 5$, find the value of x when $y = 10$.

Q12 If y and x vary inversely, and $y = 12$ when $x = 3$ find:
  a) the value of x when $y = 9$
  b) the value of y when $x = 6$.

Q13 On a daytrip, a man takes 2 hours to get to the seaside from his home, travelling at 72 km per hour. If he can do the return journey at a speed of 80 km per hour, how long will it take him?

Q14 Given that $y \propto \dfrac{1}{x}$, complete this table of values.

Put the numbers into the equation $y = k/x$ to find the value of k. Then you can find the rest of the ys.

x	1	2	3	4	5	6
y					9.6	

Make sure you know the 4 main details about Direct and Inverse Proportion:
1) what happens when one quantity increases,
2) the graph,
3) the table of values and
4) whether it's the ratio or the product that's the same for all values.

Q15 The area of a circle is proportional to the square of the radius. If the area is 113 cm² when the radius is 6 cm, find:
  a) the area of a circle with radius 5 cm
  b) the radius of a circle with area 29 cm².
    Give your answers to 1 d.p.

Q16 If $y \propto x^2$ and $y = 4$ when $x = 4$, find the value of y when $x = 12$.

Q17 $y = kx^3$ and $y = 200$ when $x = 5$.
  a) Find the value of k.
  b) Find the value of y when $x = 8$.
  c) Find the value of x when $y = 2433.4$.

Direct and Inverse Proportion

Q18 Given that y varies inversely as the square of x, complete the following table of values, given that x is always positive.

X	1	2	5	
y			4	1

X	2			8
y	24	6	$2\frac{2}{3}$	

Q19 Two cylindrical containers are filled to the same depth, d cm, with water. The mass of the water in each container is proportional to the square of the radius of each container. The first container has a radius of 16 cm and the water has a mass of 16 kg. If the second container has a radius of 8 cm, find the mass of the water inside it.

r = 16 cm

r = 8 cm

Q20 Given that r varies inversely as the square of s, and $r = 24$ when $s = 10$, find the values of:
a) r when $s = 5$
b) s when $r = 150$, given that s is positive
c) r when $s = 2$
d) s when $r = 37\frac{1}{2}$, given that s is negative

Don't forget about that little joker, the "inverse square" variation — they'll expect you to know that, too.

Q21 The gravitational pull of the Earth is inversely proportional to the square of the distance from the centre of the Earth. At the Earth's surface (approx. 6371 km from the centre) the gravitational pull is around 9.8 N kg^{-1}. When launching a satellite into space, the gravitational pull helps determine the orbit. What would be the gravitational pull on a satellite at a height of 100 km above the Earth's surface (to 1 d.p)?

Q22 By considering the values in the table, decide whether $y \propto x$, $y \propto \frac{1}{x}$ or $y \propto \frac{1}{x^2}$.

a) Write down the equation which shows how y varies with x.
b) Find the value of y when $x = 6.4$
c) Find the value of x when $y = 16$.

X	1.2	2.5	3.2	4.8
y	$166\frac{2}{3}$	80	62.5	$41\frac{2}{3}$

Symmetry

It seems to me that trouble comes in pairs... and now you've got to learn two types of symmetry — but don't worry, I reckon their names pretty much give the game away.

You need to know TWO types of symmetry:	
1) LINE SYMMETRY	You can draw a mirror line across the object and both sides will fold together exactly.
2) ROTATIONAL SYMMETRY	You can rotate the shape or drawing into different positions that all look exactly the same.

Q1 Draw <u>all</u> the lines of symmetry for each of the following shapes.
(Some shapes may have no lines of symmetry)

a)   b)   c)   d)   e)   f)

These questions are a piece of cake if you use tracing paper — and remember you can use it in the Exam, so take some with you or ask for it.

Q2 What is the <u>order of rotational symmetry</u> for each of the following shapes?

a)   b)   c)   d)

Q3 Mark in the <u>lines of symmetry</u> of the following letters. State the <u>order</u> of rotational symmetry for each one.

MHVBAKZ

Q4 Draw an example of each of the following shapes. Put in the <u>axes of symmetry</u> and state the <u>order</u> of rotational symmetry.

a) An equilateral triangle.
b) An isosceles triangle.
c) A rhombus.
d) An isosceles trapezium.
e) A regular octagon.
f) A parallelogram.

Perimeters and Areas

Q1   Calculate the area and perimeter of the rectangle.

4 cm

6 cm

5 cm

Q2   Calculate the area and perimeter of the square.

Q3   You have been asked to paint the outside wall
of a building shown in the diagram opposite.
a) Find the area of wall that needs painting.
b) A 1 litre tin of paint will cover 13 m².
How many 1 litre tins are needed to give the
wall two coats of paint?
c) The wall is also going to have a tiled border
around the edge. Calculate the length of the
edge of the wall to be tiled.

All measurements in m

You need the two circle formulas here
— C = π × d and
A = π × r².

Q4   A rectangular dining room, with a width equal
to half its length, needs carpet tiling.
a) Calculate the area of the floor, if its width is 12 m.
b) If carpet tiles are 50 cm by 50 cm squares,
calculate how many tiles will be required.
c) If carpet tiles cost £4.99 per m²,
calculate the <u>cost</u> of tiling the dining room.

Q5   An attachment on a child's toy is made from plastic
in the shape of an octagon with a square cut out.
By counting squares or otherwise, find the area of
plastic needed to make 4 of these attachments.

2 cm

4.24 cm

4 cm

2 cm

4 cm

2 cm

4.24 cm

2 cm

Q6   Josh is making a cube bean bag out of material
for his textiles coursework. If each side of the
cube is to have edges of length 60 cm, how
many <u>square metres</u> of material will Josh need?

Q7   Natasha is training for a marathon by jogging around the outside of a square
field of area 9000 m². One evening, Natasha completed 11 laps of the field.
How far did she run? Give your answer to the nearest 100 m.

Q8   A lawn is to be made 48 m². If its width is 5 m, how long is it? How many rolls of turf
50 cm wide and 11 m long should be ordered to grass this area?

Q9   This parallelogram has an area of 4773 mm².
How long is its <u>base</u>?

43 mm

87 mm

base

Perimeters and Areas

Q10   A metal blade for a craft knife is the
shape of a <u>trapezium</u>.
Calculate the area of the metal.

If you can't remember the formula for the area of a trapezium,
you can always split the shape into a rectangle and a triangle.

Q11   Jon is making a metal bracket as part of his technology project.
The bracket is stamped out of sheet metal in a 2 phase process:
1st: The <u>outer triangle</u>, measuring 14.4 cm by 10 cm,
is stamped out.
2nd: A smaller <u>inner triangle</u> measuring 5.76 cm by 4 cm
is stamped out of the larger triangle.
The bracket should be made from no more than 50 cm^2
of sheet metal if the fixing is to support its weight.
Will the fixing take the weight of Jon's bracket?

Q12   A modern glass sculpture is to be erected.
It is made from glass in the shape of two mountain peaks.
Calculate each <u>separate</u> area and hence
find the <u>total</u> area of glass required.

Q13   A fighter aircraft's wing is shown on the right.
Calculate its <u>area</u>, and its <u>perimeter</u>.

Two lots of Pythagoras are needed
to find the length of the third side.

Q14   A simple tent is to be made in the shape of a
triangular prism. The dimensions are shown
in the diagram.
  a) The two end faces are isosceles triangles.
Find their areas.
  b) The two sides and ground sheet are
rectangles. Find their areas.
  c) How much material is required to make
this tent?

Q15   Calculate the area of a <u>rhombus</u> with diagonals
7 km by 11 km.

Solids and Nets

Before you go any further — make sure you know these 3 facts...

Surface Area and Nets

1) <u>SURFACE AREA</u> only applies to solid 3-D objects. It's the <u>TOTAL AREA</u> of all the <u>OUTER SURFACES</u> added together.
2) A <u>NET</u> is just A <u>SOLID SHAPE</u> folded out <u>FLAT</u>.
3) SURFACE AREA OF SOLID = AREA OF NET.

There are 4 nets that you need to know inside out... so to speak: **1) Triangular Prism, 2) Cube, 3) Cuboid, 4) Pyramid.** I reckon you shouldn't read any further till you're 100% happy with them.

Q1 The net shown will fold to make a cube. Only one flap is shown. <u>Copy</u> the diagram.

a) Put an X in each corner that touches Y when the cube is made up.

b) Put an F where the flap will join one face to another when the cube is made up.

c) Put on the other flaps necessary to glue the cube together.

Q2 Draw an <u>accurate</u> net that would fold to make the 3-D cuboid shown (diagram is not full size). It is not necessary to include flaps.

Q3 Draw a <u>full size net</u> (without flaps) of a square-based pyramid whose base has sides of length 3 cm.

Q4 Julie is designing new packaging boxes for her home-made jewellery. Draw <u>accurately</u> the net of a regular tetrahedron, with sufficient flaps to glue it together.

Q5 a) What shape is the <u>base</u> of the cuboid shown opposite?
b) Which edges are the same length as DE?
c) Which lengths equal CE?
d) Which lengths equal the diagonal DG?
e) How many vertices does the cuboid have?

Q6 Draw a <u>cone</u>.
a) How many vertices does it have?
b) How many edges?

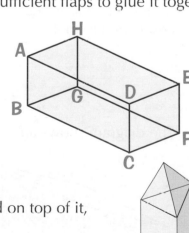

Q7 An equilateral triangular prism has a tetrahedron placed on top of it, as shown. For this <u>combined</u> solid,
a) How many edges does it have?
b) How many vertices?
c) How many faces?

UNIT 3 — GEOMETRY AND ALGEBRA

Solids and Nets

Q8

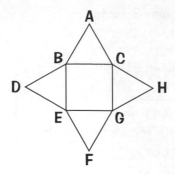

The diagram shows the net of a solid in which ABC is an equilateral triangle and BCGE is a square.
a) Which points will coincide with A when the net is folded up to make the solid?
b) Describe the symmetry of the net.
c) How many faces, edges and vertices does it have when in solid form?

Q9   The diagram shows the net of a cube of edge 8 cm.

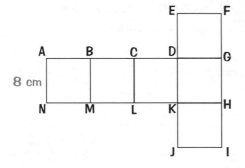

a) Which point coincides with M when the net is folded to make the cube?
b) Find the area of the face DGHK.
c) What is the total surface area of the cube?
d) Draw a 3-D scale drawing of the completed cube.

Q10

This diagram shows a net for a rectangular box with a lid. For the same box sketch a different net.

Q11   Which of these two nets will form a pyramid on a triangular base with all four faces equilateral triangles?

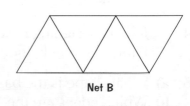

Net A

Net B

Q12   The diagram shows an isometric projection of a triangular prism.

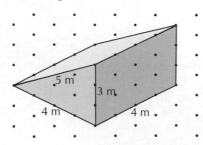

5 m

3 m

4 m   4 m

Draw:
a) the front elevation
b) the side elevation
c) the plan.

Surface Area and Volume

Make sure you know the <u>4 main volume formulas</u> — for <u>spheres</u>, <u>prisms</u>, <u>pyramids</u>, <u>cones</u>.

Q1 Joe buys a polythene tunnel to protect his plants from frost. It has a semicircular diameter of 70 cm and a length of 3 m.

a) Find the cross-sectional area.

b) Hence find the volume of the tunnel.

3 m

70 cm

Q2 I am planning to build a circular pond in my garden surrounded by a ring shaped paved area.
The pond will be 50 cm deep and filled with water.

a) Calculate the approximate cost of paving the area around the pond with slabs costing £16 per m². Give your answer to the nearest £10.

b) I need to add 15 ml of liquid pond treatment for every m³ of water in the pond. Find the volume of treatment I will need to add to the pond. Give your answer to the nearest ml.

paved area

4 m

5 m

Q3 A solid metal cube, each of whose sides is 10 cm long, is melted down and made into a solid cylinder 10 cm high.

a) What is the radius of this cylinder?

b) Find the surface area of the cylinder.

10 cm

10 cm

10 cm

10 cm

Q4 A tin mug has the dimensions shown.

a) What is the greatest volume of milk the mug can hold?

b) In fact, 600 cm³ of milk is poured in. How high will it go up the mug?

16 cm

←10 cm→

Q5

3 cm

3 cm

5 mm

A nut has the cross-section illustrated. The circular hole has a diameter of 1.4 cm and the nut is 5 mm thick. Find the volume of the nut in cm³.

(Units...)

Surface Area and Volume

Q6 Water is flowing into each of these containers at a constant rate.
For each container, sketch the graph of the depth of water against time.

Container A

Depth

Time

Container B

Depth

Time

Q7 Steve has bought a pair of speaker stands. The base of
each stand is a hollow prism with the dimensions shown.
A hollow tube of diameter 4 cm and height 110 cm
screws into the top of each base to form the stand.

Steve is filling the stands with sand to improve stability.
Find the volume of sand Steve needs to use to fill both
stands (the bases __and__ the tubes).
Give your answer in litres to 2 d.p.

14 cm
6 cm
20 cm
20 cm

1 litre = 1000 cm³

Q8

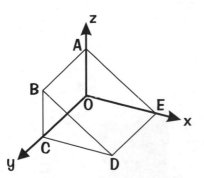

30 cm
90 cm
60 cm
30 cm
1 m

Jill buys a bookshelf with the dimensions shown in the diagram.
a) Find the cross-sectional area.
b) Find the volume of the bookshelf in m³.

Q9

z
A
B
O
E
x
C
y
D

The diagram shows a triangular prism.
The coordinates of A are (0, 0, 5).
The coordinates of E are (4, 0, 0).
The coordinates of C are (0, 8, 0).
a) Write down the coordinates of:
  i) B
  ii) D.
b) Calculate the volume of the prism.

Q10 Bill has a greenhouse with dimensions as shown.
The roof is made up of eight panels of equal size.

A storm breaks all of the glass in the shaded area on
the diagram.

Calculate the area of glass which Bill must buy to
repair his greenhouse.

E
A
B
4 m
2.5 m
5 m
D
4 m
C

Look for a right-angled triangle to calculate AB.

Surface Area and Volume

Q11

2.6 cm

1.8 cm

1.2 cm

An egg timer is symmetrical and consists of hemispheres, cylinders and cones joined together as shown to the left.

a) Calculate the volume of sand in the upper container.

> You need to find three volumes and add them together.

Sand runs into the bottom container at a constant rate of 0.05 cm³ per second. At the end of a certain time period the sand has fallen through into the bottom container as shown to the right.

0.3 cm

1.2 cm

h

b) How high (*h*) has it risen up the cylindrical part of the bottom container?

c) How long has it taken the sand to fall through until it is at this height?

Q12

5 cm

2 cm

10 cm

chocolate

4 cm

An ice-cream cone is 10 cm deep and has a base diameter of 5 cm. The bottom 4 cm of the cone is filled with solid chocolate as shown. The rest of the cone is filled with ice cream and a hemisphere of ice cream is mounted on top so that the base of the hemisphere coincides with the base of the cone.

a) Calculate the volume of ice cream required to make one ice cream.

b) Calculate the outer surface area of the cone.

Q13

20 cm

10 cm

10 cm

Mike and Shelly are doing an experiment to find the radius of a marble. They fill a cylindrical container of diameter 10 cm and height 20 cm with water to a depth of 10 cm. 200 identical marbles are now submerged in the water. The depth increases to 14.5 cm. Calculate the radius of one marble.

> The volume increase is a cylinder and you're told the height.

Q14 A cuboid has a height of *x* m, a width of (3 – *x*) m and a length of (5 – *x*) m.

a) Write down an expression for the volume of the cuboid.

b) Complete the table of values using your expression for the volume of the cuboid.

x	0	1	2	3
V			6	

c) Draw a graph of V against *x* for 0 ≤ *x* ≤ 3.

d) Use your graph to estimate the maximum volume of the cuboid.

e) Estimate the surface area of the cuboid when the volume is at its maximum.

f) A particular cuboid has a volume of 6 m³. By using your graph to find the two possible values of *x*, estimate the maximum total surface area of the cuboid for this volume.

V

10

8

6

4

2

0

1   2   3   4   x

Length, Area and Volume Formulas

Time to get your brain in gear — these can get pretty confusing...

You need to know these three facts:

1) LENGTH FORMULAS always have LENGTHS OCCURRING SINGLY
2) AREA FORMULAS always have lengths MULTIPLIED IN PAIRS
3) VOLUME FORMULAS always have lengths multiplied in GROUPS OF THREE

Q1 p, q and r are lengths. State for each of the following whether the formula gives a <u>length</u>, an <u>area</u>, a <u>volume</u> or <u>none of these</u>:

a) $p + q$

b) $pq - rq$

c) $p^2q^2 + pr^2$

d) pr/q

e) $5pqr/10$

f) $\pi pqr/2$

g) $p^3 + q^3 + r^3$

h) $9pr^2 - 2q$

Q2 w, x, y and z are lengths. State for each of the following, whether the formula gives a <u>length</u>, an <u>area</u> or a <u>volume</u>, when numbers are substituted in for the variables:

a) $\dfrac{xy}{w}$

b) $\dfrac{xy^2 - w^2y}{z^2}$

c) $\dfrac{x^3}{y} - 14wz$

d) $\dfrac{x^2}{w} + \dfrac{w^2}{y} + \dfrac{y^2}{z} + \dfrac{z^3}{x^2}$

Q3 a, b, and c are lengths, r is the radius, $\pi = 3.14$.
State whether each of the following formulas give a <u>perimeter</u>, <u>area</u> or <u>neither</u> of these.

a) $3\pi r^2 + abc$

b) $6\pi r + a - 6c$

c) $17ab + \pi r^2$

d) $\dfrac{16abc}{8b}$

Q4 If r is a length, is $\dfrac{4}{3}\pi r^2$ a volume formula?

Q5 If b and h are lengths, is $\frac{1}{2}bh$ an area formula?

Q6 Is $\dfrac{h}{2}(x + y)$ an area formula if x, y and h are lengths?

> **Remember** —
> if r is a length,
> then r² is an area
> and r³ is a volume.

Q7 If x and h are lengths, could this be a perimeter formula: $x + x + h + h + h$?

Q8 Could $\frac{1}{2}Dd$ be a volume formula, given that D and d are lengths?

Q9 The following statements are <u>incomplete</u>. For each one, find out what is missing and rewrite the formula correctly:

a) Volume of a cube = l (where l is the length)

b) Area of a circle = $\pi\dfrac{d}{2}$ (where d is the diameter)

c) Perimeter of a circle = πr (where r is the radius)

If you ever see something like r⁶ then rub your eyes because it's gone wrong — unless you're an alien from a 6-dimensional universe, in which case you'll feel right at home.

Geometry

Here are some angle rules then — just the 7 for now. You can't get away without knowing these, I'm afraid, so get learning.

1) Angles in a triangle <u>add up to 180°</u>

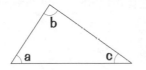

2) Angles in a 4-sided shape <u>add up to 360°</u>

3) Angles round a point <u>add up to 360°</u>

4) When a line crosses <u>TWO PARALLEL LINES</u>, the two bunches of angles are the same

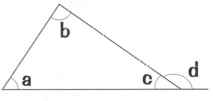

5) Angles on a straight line <u>add up to 180°</u>

6) <u>ISOSCELES TRIANGLES</u> have two sides the same and two angles the same

7) <u>EXTERIOR</u> angle of a triangle = sum of opposite <u>INTERIOR</u> angles.

$$d = a + b$$

For the following diagrams, find the <u>lettered</u> angles. LM is a straight line.

Q1 a)   b)   c)   d)

Q2 a)   b)   c)   d)

Geometry

This page is a bit dull — just lots of boring angles... still, that's geometry for you. Oh and by the way, you've got to work the angles out — don't try and sneakily measure them, they're probably drawn wrong anyway...

For the following diagrams, find the <u>lettered</u> angles.   LM is a straight line.

Q3 a)
b)
c)
d)

Q4 a)
b)
c)

```
\ \ \ \ \ \ \ \ \ \ \ \ \ \ \ \ \ \ \ \ \ \ \ \ \ \
Keep an eye out for parallel lines — they'll help no end...
as long as you can remember the angle rules, of course.
/ / / / / / / / / / / / / / / / / / / / / / / / / /
```

Q5 a)
b)
c)

Q6 a)
b)
c)

Regular Polygons

The one thing they're <u>guaranteed</u> to ask you about is <u>Interior and Exterior Angles</u> — you'd better get learning those formulas...

> A <u>POLYGON</u> is a many-sided shape. A <u>REGULAR</u> polygon is one where <u>ALL THE SIDES AND ANGLES ARE THE SAME</u>.
>
> You need to know these two formulas:
> 1) EXTERIOR ANGLE = 360° ÷ No. of Sides
> 2) INTERIOR ANGLE = 180° − EXTERIOR ANGLE

Q1 What sort of triangles occur in every <u>regular polygon</u> (<u>except</u> a hexagon), when each vertex is joined to the centre by a straight line?

Q2 Using a compass, construct an <u>equilateral</u> triangle with sides of 3 cm. What is the interior angle at each vertex?

Q3 Sketch a regular hexagon and draw in all its lines of symmetry. State the order of <u>rotational</u> symmetry.

Q4 In each of the pentagons below, all the sides are of equal length, two of the angles are 90° and the other interior angles are m, m, and r degrees.

    a) Explain in <u>two</u> different ways why $2m + r = 360°$.

    b) What is the size of the exterior angle x?

    c) Copy the diagram and add two more pentagons (by tracing through) so that the point T is completely surrounded and the whole figure forms part of a tessellation. Label all the angles of the new pentagons.

Q5 A square and a regular hexagon are placed adjacent to each other.

    a) What is the size of ∠PQW?

    b) What is the size of ∠PRW?

    c) How many sides has the regular polygon that has ∠PQW as one of its angles?

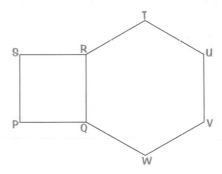

Q6 An <u>irregular pentagon</u> has interior angles of 100°, 104°, 120°. If the other two angles are equal, what is their size?

Q7 **a)** The <u>sum</u> of the <u>interior</u> angles of a <u>regular</u> 24-sided polygon is 3960°. Use this to calculate the size of one <u>interior</u> angle.

    b) From your answer to part **a)** calculate one <u>exterior</u> angle and show that the <u>sum</u> of the exterior angles equals 360°.

Regular Polygons

Q8

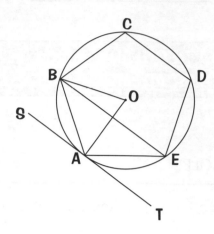

ABCDE is a regular pentagon. It is drawn in a circle centre O. SAT is a tangent drawn to the circle at A.

a) Calculate the size of angle BOA.

b) Find the size of angle OBA.

c) Write down the size of angle:

   i) SAO

   ii) BAS.

d) Hence write down the size of angle BEA giving a reason for your answer.

Q9 The sum of the interior angles of a regular polygon is 2520°. How many sides does this regular polygon have?

Remember that formula for the sum of interior angles — it comes in handy here.

Q10

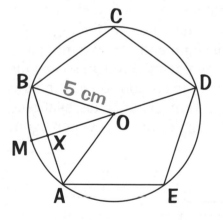

ABCDE is a regular pentagon whose vertices lie on a circle of radius 5 cm, centre O. DOM is an axis of symmetry of the pentagon and cuts the chord AB at X.

a) Calculate the size of angle BOX.

b) Find the length OX. Hence find the distance of M from the chord AB.

You need to use trigonometry to find OX — Cos θ = adj / hyp.

Q11 ABCDEFGH is a regular octagon.

a) Copy the figure and mark on the axis of symmetry which maps H to A.

b) Calculate the size of angle EFC.

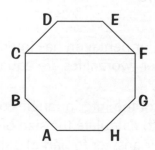

Circle Geometry

Q1 Using π = 3.14, find:
a) The area of a circle with radius = 6.12 m. Give your answer <u>to 3 dp</u>.
b) The circumference of a circle with radius = 7.2 m. Give your answer <u>to 2 sf</u>.
c) The circumference of a circle with diameter = 14.8 m. Give your answer <u>to 1 dp</u>.
d) The area of a circle with diameter = 4.246 cm. Give your answer <u>to 3 dp</u>.

Q2 Find the <u>area and the perimeter</u> of each of the shapes drawn here. Use π = 3.14.

a)

b)

c)

Q3 A plastic strip is made in the shape shown. The curves AC and BD are both arcs of circles with centre O. The larger circle has radius 30 mm and the smaller circle has radius 20 mm. The shaded ends of the shape are both semicircles.

a) Find the area of the shape ABDC.
b) Find the area of the two semicircular ends. Hence write down the area of the complete shape.

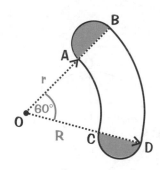

Suppose the radius of the arc AC is now r and that of BD is R.
c) Write down a formula for the area of the sector OBD in terms of R.
d) Write down an expression for the area of the shape ABDC in terms of r and R.
e) Hence write down an expression for the area of the complete shape.

Q4

Side View

A washing powder ball looks from the side like a circle with the shaded area removed. The circle has radius 5 cm and the angle AOB = 80°.
a) Find the area of the sector OAB.
b) Find the area of triangle AOB and hence the area of the shaded area.

The formula you need for part b) is area = ½absin(C).

Circle Geometry

Q5 ABCD is a cyclic quadrilateral with angle BCD = 100°.
EF is a tangent to the circle touching it at A.
Angle DAF = 30°.
Write down the size of angle:

a) BAD

b) EAB.

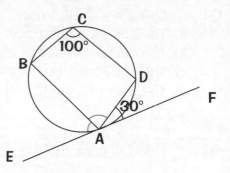

Q6 A, B, and C are points on the circumference of a circle with
centre O. BD and CD are tangents of the circle.

a) State the length BD.

b) Calculate the angle COD.

c) State the angle COB.

d) Find the angle CAB.

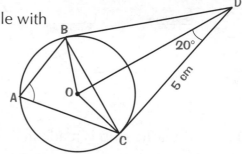

Q7 A, B, C, D and E are points on the circumference of
a circle with centre O. Angle BDE = 53°. The line
AF is a tangent to the circle, touching it at A.
Angle EAF = 32°. Find:

a) angle BOE

b) angle ACE.

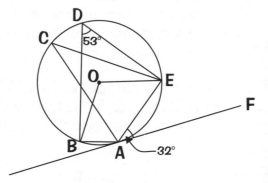

Q8 ABCD is a cyclic quadrilateral and the tangent
to the circle at A makes an angle of 70° with the
side AD. Angle BCA = 30°. Write down, giving
a reason, the size of:

a) angle ACD

b) angle BAD.

Q9

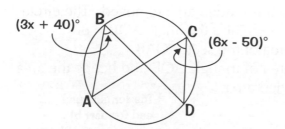

A, B, C and D are points on the
circumference of a circle. Angle ABD
= (3x + 40)° and angle ACD = (6x – 50)°.

a) Give a reason why angle ABD
and angle ACD are the same.

b) Form an equation in x and by solving it,
find the size of angle ABD.

Circle Geometry

Q10   O is the centre of a circle and AB is a chord.
The length OA = 5 cm and angle OAB = 20°.
Find the length of the chord AB.

One way to do this is to work out angle AOB and use the cine rule.

Q11   A, B, C and D are points on the circumference
of a circle. O is the centre of the circle and
angle AOD = 140°. Write down:
a) angle ABD
b) angle ABC
c) angle DBC.

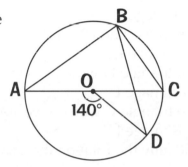

Q12   A tangent of a circle is drawn, touching it at A.
C and B are two other points on the circumference
and AOB is a diameter. O is the centre of the circle.
Angle ABC is 23°.
a) Write down the size of angle ACB, giving a reason
for your answer.
b) Find the size of the angle marked x° in the diagram.

Q13

ABCD is a cyclic quadrilateral. The lines AC and BD
intersect at X. Lengths AX = 4 cm, DX = 8 cm and
XC = 10 cm. Angles DXC = 85° and ABD = 30°.
a) Show that triangles DXC and AXB are similar.
b) Find the length of XB.
c) Write down the size of angle BDC.

Q14   B, C and D are three points on the circumference of
a circle with BD as a diameter. O is the centre of the
circle and ADC is a straight line.
AB = 10 cm and BC = 3 cm.
a) Write down the size of angle ACB, giving a
reason for your answer.
b) Show that AC is 9.54 cm correct to 2 decimal places.
c) If AD = 5 cm, find the length of the diameter DOB correct to 2 decimal places.

The Four Transformations

Only 4 of these to learn... and good old **TERRY**'s always around to help if you need him.

Q1 Copy the axes and mark on triangle A
with corners (-1, 2), (0, 4) and (-2, 4).
Use a scale of 1 cm to 1 unit.

a) Reflect A in the line $y = -x$.
Label this image B.

b) Reflect A in the line $x = 1$.
Label the image C.

c) Reflect A in the line $y = -1$.
Label the image D.

d) Translate triangle D with the vector $\binom{4}{2}$.
Label this image E.

e) Translate triangle C with the vector $\binom{3}{-3}$.
Label this image F.

f) Describe fully the rotation that sends
C to E.

It helps to label the corners of
the triangle so you can see
exactly what goes where when
you do the transformations.

Q2 Copy the axes using a scale of 1 cm to
1 unit. Mark on the axes a quadrilateral
Q with corners (-2, 1), (-3, 1), (-3, 3)
and (-2, 3).

a) Rotate Q clockwise through 90°
about the point (-1, 2). Label the
image R.

b) Rotate R clockwise through 90°
about the point (0, 1). Label the
image S.

c) Describe fully the rotation that
maps Q to S.

d) Rotate Q through 180° about the
point (-½, -1). Label the image T.

e) Rotate Q anticlockwise through 90°
about the point (-1, -1). Label the
image U.

f) Describe fully the rotation that sends U to T.

The Four Transformations

Move each point separately — then check your shape hasn't
done anything unexpected while you weren't looking.

Q3 Copy the axes below using a scale of 1 cm to 1 unit.

A parallelogram A has
vertices at (6, 4), (10, 4),
(8, 10) and (12, 10).
Draw this parallelogram
onto your axes.
An enlargement scale factor
½ and centre (0, 0)
transforms parallelogram
A onto its image B.

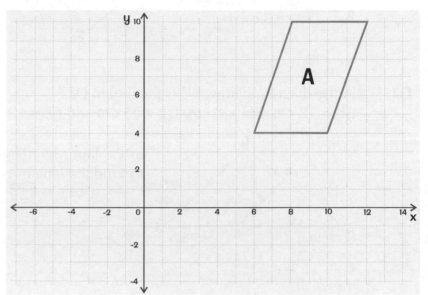

a) Draw this image B on
your axes.

b) Translate B by the vector
$\left(\begin{smallmatrix} -3 \\ -2 \end{smallmatrix}\right)$ and label this image C.

c) Calculate the ratio of the
area of parallelogram C to
the area of parallelogram A.

Q4 A is the point (4, 3), B is (4, 1) and
C is (5, 1).

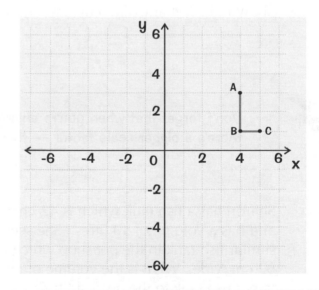

a) Using a scale of 1 cm to 1 unit
draw the axes and mark on it
the figure given by ABC.

b) Reflect ABC in the x-axis and
label the image $A_1B_1C_1$.

c) Reflect $A_1B_1C_1$ in the y-axis and
label the image $A_2B_2C_2$.

d) Describe fully the single transformation
which would map ABC onto $A_2B_2C_2$.

Q5 Draw axes with x and y running from 0 to 12 with a scale of 1 cm to 1 unit.
O is the origin. $\overrightarrow{OP} = \left(\begin{smallmatrix} 4 \\ 2 \end{smallmatrix}\right)$, $\overrightarrow{PQ} = \left(\begin{smallmatrix} -1 \\ 2 \end{smallmatrix}\right)$, and $\overrightarrow{QR} = 2\overrightarrow{OP}$.

a) Mark P, Q and R on your axes.

b) Translate R by $\overrightarrow{QO}$. Label the image T.

c) Verify that $\overrightarrow{PQ} + \overrightarrow{QR} + \overrightarrow{RT} + \overrightarrow{TP} = O$.

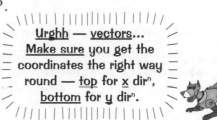

Urghh — vectors...
Make sure you get the
coordinates the right way
round — top for x dir^n,
bottom for y dir^n.

Congruence, Similarity and Enlargement

Q1   Which pair of triangles are congruent? Explain why.

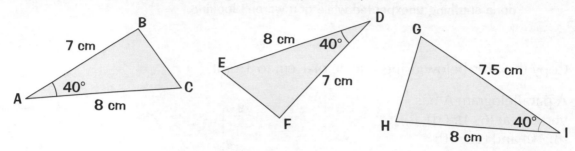

Q2   In the diagram below, BC is parallel to DE.
AB = 12 cm, BD = 8 cm, DE = 25 cm and CE = 10 cm.

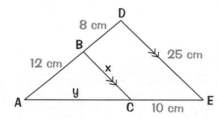

a) Explain why triangles ABC and ADE are similar.
b) Find the lengths of *x* and *y* in the diagram.

Q3   Another triangle, congruent to the triangle shown on the
right, must be drawn with vertices at three of the dots.
Show in how many different ways this can be done.

 **Don't forget that when you're enlarging areas and volumes,
there's a bigger scale factor — that one catches everyone out.**

Q4   Sharon has a fish tank which is 42 cm wide
and has a volume of 30 litres. She sees a
similar fish tank in the pet shop which is
63 cm wide. What is the volume of the
larger fish tank to the nearest litre?

Q5   A cylindrical bottle can hold 1 litre of oil. A second cylindrical bottle has
twice the radius but the same height. It also contains oil.
a) Explain why these bottles are not similar.
b) How much oil can the larger bottle hold?

Congruence, Similarity and Enlargement

Q6 A boy made a symmetrical framework with metal rods as shown. Lengths AB = BC, ST = TC and AP = PQ. Angle BVC = 90° and length BV = 9 cm.

a) Find two triangles which are similar to triangle ABC.

b) Calculate the length of AP. Hence write down the length of PT.

c) Calculate the area of triangle ABC.

d) Find the area of triangle APQ. Give your answer correct to 3 significant figures.

e) Hence write down the area of PQBST correct to 2 significant figures.

Q7 For a graphics project, Eliza makes a model of a chocolates box in the shape of a cuboid 5 cm long, 2 cm wide and 3 cm high.

a) Calculate the area of material needed to make the model (assuming no flaps are required for gluing).

b) Eliza decides that the full size packaging will be similar to the model, but enlarged by a scale factor of 4. Calculate the area of material Eliza needs to make a full-size box.

Q8 Using the point O as centre of enlargement draw accurately and label:

a) the image $A_1B_1C_1$ of the triangle ABC after an enlargement scale factor 2

b) the image $A_2B_2C_2$ of the triangle ABC after an enlargement scale factor -1.

c) Which image is congruent to triangle ABC?

Q9 On a holiday near the sea, children built a sandcastle in the shape of a cone. The radius of the base is 100 cm and the height is 100 cm.

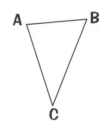

a) What is the volume of the sandcastle in m³ correct to 3 significant figures?
The children now remove the top portion to make a similar cone but only 50 cm in height.

b) State the radius of the base of this smaller cone.

c) State the ratio of the volume of the small cone to the volume of the original cone.

d) Calculate the volume of the small cone in m³ correct to 3 significant figures.

e) Hence write down the ratio of the volume of the portion left of the original cone to the smaller cone in the form n:1.

Pythagoras and Bearings

Don't try and do it all in your head — you've got to label the sides
or you're bound to mess it up. Go on, get your pen out...

Q1   Find the length of the hypotenuse in each of the following triangles.

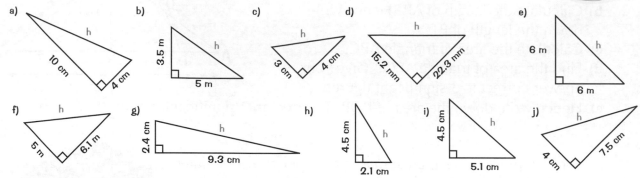

Q2   Find the length of the shorter side in each of the following triangles.

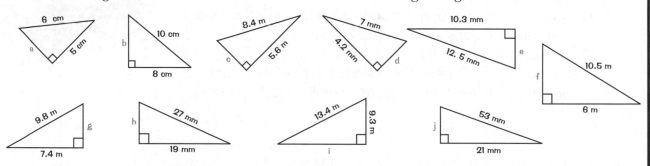

Q3   Find the unknown length in each of the following triangles.

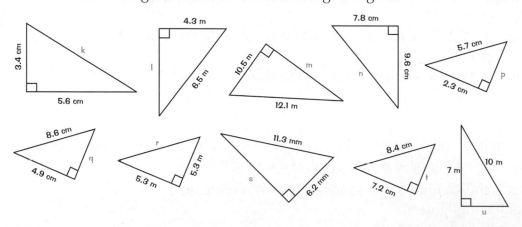

Q4   Calculate the bearings required in these diagrams.

It's easy to get lost if you don't follow
the easy rule: always measure
bearings from the <u>north line</u>.

Pythagoras and Bearings

Q5   A window cleaner wants to clean the upstairs windows of an office.
To meet safety regulations, his 10 m long ladder needs to be angled
so that the bottom of the ladder is at least 2.6 m away from the wall.
What is the maximum height that the top of the ladder can reach
when used safely? Give your answer to 1 decimal place.

Q6   A rectangular field is 250 m by 190 m. How far is it across diagonally?

Q7   **a)** Calculate the lengths WY and ZY.
b) What is the total distance WXYZW?
c) What is the area of quadrilateral WXYZ?

Q8   A plane flies due east for 153 km then turns and flies due north for 116 km.
How far is it now from where it started?

Q9   A coastguard spots a boat on a bearing of 040° and at a distance of 350 m.
He can also see a tree due east of him. The tree is due south of the boat.
a) Draw a scale diagram and measure accurately the distances from the:
i) boat to the tree
ii) coastguard to the tree
b) Check by Pythagoras to see if your answers are reasonable.

The word "<u>from</u>" is the most important word in a bearings
question, so look out for it — it tells you where to start <u>from</u>.

Q10   Four towns W, X, Y and Z are situated as follows:
W is 90 km north of X, Y is on a bearing 175° and 165 km from X, X is on a
bearing 129° and 123 km from Z. Draw an accurate scale diagram to represent
the situation.
From your drawing measure the distances:
a) WZ   **b)** WY   **c)** ZY.
Measure the bearings:
d) Y from Z   **e)** W from Z   **f)** Y from W.

Q11   A walker travels 1200 m on a bearing of 165° and then
another 1500 m on a bearing of 210°. By accurate
measurement, find how far she is now from her starting
point. What bearing must she walk on to return to base?

Q12   A fishing boat travels at 12 km/h for an hour due north. It then turns due west
and travels at 7 km/h for an hour. How far is it from its starting point now?
What bearing must it travel on to return to base?

Trigonometry

Before you start a trigonometry question, write down the ratios, using
SOH CAH TOA (Sockatoa!) — it'll help you pick your formula.

Q1 Calculate the tan, sin and cos of each of these angles:
a) 17°   **b)** 83°   **c)** 5°   **d)** 28°   **e)** 45°.

Q2 Use the tangent ratio to find the unknowns:

Q3 Use the cosine ratio to find the unknowns:

Q4 Use the sine ratio to find the unknowns:

Q5 Find the unknowns using the appropriate ratios:

Trigonometry

Q6 A right-angled triangle has sides measuring 30 m, 40 m and 50 m.
  a) Draw a rough sketch of the triangle, clearly labelling the hypotenuse.
  b) Calculate the size of the smallest angle.

> Make sure you've got the hang of the inverse SIN, COS and TAN functions on your calc... and check it's in DEG mode or you'll get nowhere fast.

Q7 The points P(1, 2), Q(4, 2) and R(4, -3) when joined together form a right-angled triangle.
  a) Draw a rough sketch of the triangle, labelling the length of each side.
  b) Without measuring, calculate the angle RPQ.
  c) Deduce angle PRQ.

Q8 The points A(1, -2), B(4, -1) and C(1, 3) are the vertices of the triangle ABC.
  a) On graph paper, plot the points A, B and C.
  b) By adding a suitable horizontal line, or otherwise, calculate the angle CAB.
  c) Similarly calculate the angle ACB.
  d) By using the fact that the interior angles of a triangle add up to 180° work out the angle ABC.

Q9 Mary was lying on the floor looking up at the star on top of her Christmas tree. She looked up through an angle of 55° when she was 1.5 m from the base of the tree. How high was the star?

Q10 Geoff is tiling his bathroom. He needs to cut off the right-angled triangle shown so that the tiles will fit nicely on his wall. Calculate the angle, θ, he needs to cut the tile at. Give your answer to the nearest degree.

Q11 Mr Brown took his dog for a walk in the park. The dog's lead was 2 m long. The dog ran 0.7 m from the path Mr Brown was walking on.

What angle did the lead make with the path?

Q12 A boat travels 9 km due south and then 7 km due east. What bearing must it travel on to return to base?

Trigonometry

Q13 This isosceles triangle has a base of 28 cm and a
top angle of 54°. Calculate:

 a) the length of sides AC and BC
 b) the perpendicular height to C
 c) the area of the triangle.

Q14 An isosceles triangle has two equal sides of 7 cm and an angle between them of 65°.
Calculate the area of the triangle.

Q15 In this parallelogram the diagonal CB is at right angles to AC.
AB is 9.5 cm and ∠CAB is 60°.
Calculate:

 a) CB   **b)** BD   **c)** the area of the parallelogram.

Q16 This rhombus WXYZ has base 15 cm and diagonal
WY of 28 cm. Calculate the:

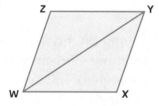

 a) length of diagonal XZ

 b) area of the rhombus

 c) angle WY makes with WX.

Q17 Two mountains are 1020 m and 1235 m high. Standing on the summit of the lower
one I look up through an angle of elevation of 16° to see the summit of the higher one.
Calculate the horizontal distance between the two mountains.

Q18 A girl is flying a kite. She holds the string, which is 45 m long, at a height of 1.3 m above
the ground. The string of the kite makes an angle of 33° with the horizontal.
What is the vertical height of the kite from the ground?

Q19 I am standing on top of an 80 m high tower. I look due north and see two cars
with angles of depression of 38° and 49°. Calculate:
 a) how far each car is from the base of the tower
 b) how far apart the cars are.

Q20 A ship sails on a bearing of 300° for 100 km. The captain can then see
a lighthouse due south of him that he knows is due west of his starting point.
Calculate how far west the lighthouse is from the ship's starting point.

3D Pythagoras and Trigonometry

Q1   The diagram shows a cuboid. Vertices A and H
have coordinates (1, 2, 8) and (4, 5, 3) respectively.
Write down the coordinates of all the other vertices.

B (.... , ... , ...)   E (.... , ... , ...)
C (.... , ... , ...)   F (.... , ... , ...)
D (.... , ... , ...)   G (.... , ... , ...)

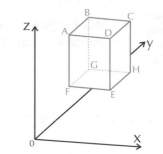

Q2   This rectangular box is 20 cm by 12 cm by 9 cm.
Calculate:

a) angle ABE
b) length AF
c) length DF
d) angle EBH.

Q3   This pyramid is on a square base of side 56 cm. Its vertical height is
32 cm. Calculate the length of:

a) the line from E to the mid-point of BC
b) the sloping edge BE.

Q4   A rectangular box measures 20 cm by 30 cm by 8 cm.
Calculate the lengths of:

a) the diagonal of each rectangular face
b) the diagonal through the centre of the box.

Q5   This glass has a radius of 2.8 cm. The straw in the glass
makes an angle of 70° with the base and protrudes 4 cm
above the rim.

a) How tall is the glass?
b) How long is the straw?

Q6   A shop sells the three different gift boxes
shown on the right. Katie wants to buy
the cheapest box that will fit a pen that is
10 cm long. Which box should she buy?

Q7   This cone has a perpendicular height of 9 cm.
The centre of the base is O. The slant line from X
makes an angle of 23° with the central axis. Calculate:

a) the radius of the base
b) the area of the base
c) the volume of the cone.

The Sine and Cosine Rules

Make sure you know the Sine Rule and <u>both forms</u> of the Cosine Rule. The one to use depends on which angles and sides you're given.

Q1 Calculate the lengths required to 3 s.f.

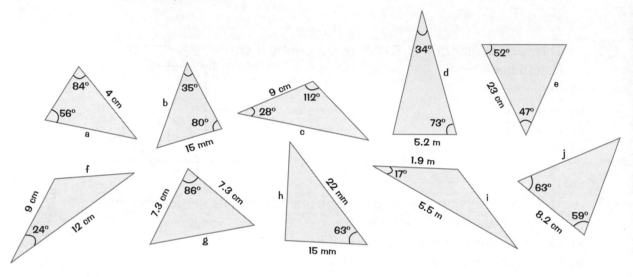

Q2 Calculate the angles required, to the nearest degree.

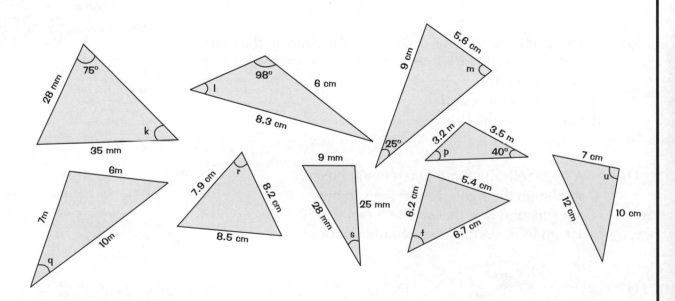

The Sine and Cosine Rules

Q3   Calculate the lettered sides and angles.

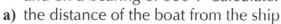

Q4   This field has measurements as shown. Calculate:
   a) ∠ZXY
   b) ∠XYZ
   c) ∠YZX.

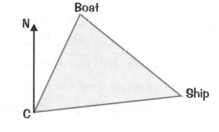

Q5   Peter is standing on a bridge over a river. He can see a tree on each bank, one 33 m and the other 35 m away from him. If he looks through an angle of 20° going from one tree to the other, how far apart are the two trees?

Q6   A coastguard sees a boat on a bearing of 038° from him and 25 km away. He also sees a ship 42 km away and on a bearing of 080°. Calculate:
   a) the distance of the boat from the ship
   b) the bearing of the boat from the ship.

Q7   An isosceles triangle has equal sides of length 7.5 cm and an angle of 56°. Sketch two possible triangles using this information and calculate the two possible lengths of the third side.

Q8   A parallelogram has sides of length 8 cm and 4.5 cm. One angle of the parallelogram is 124°. Calculate the lengths of the two diagonals.

Q9   Air traffic control are testing the reliability of their computer software by monitoring two aeroplanes and checking the computer's calculations with their own. If the horizontal distance between the planes drops to 3 miles or less, an alarm should be triggered on the computer. One of the test planes is at a distance of 5 miles from the tower, and on a bearing of 020° from the tower. The second is at a distance of 4.6 miles on a bearing of 034° and the alarm is ringing. Calculate the horizontal distance between the planes and comment on the reliability of the software.

The Sine and Cosine Rules

Q10 A vertical flagpole FP has two stay wires to the ground at A and B. They cannot be equidistant from P, as the ground is uneven. AB is 22m, ∠PAB is 34° and ∠PBA is 50°. Calculate the distances:

a) PA

b) PB.

If A is level with P and the angle of elevation of F from A is 49°, calculate:

c) FA

d) PF.

Q11 An aircraft leaves A and flies 257 km to B on a bearing of 257°. It then flies on to C, 215 km away on a bearing of 163° from B. Calculate:

a) ∠ABC

b) distance CA

c) the bearing needed to fly from A direct to C.

Q12 On my clock the hour hand is 5.5 cm, the minute hand 8 cm and the second hand 7 cm, measured from the centre. Calculate the distance between the tips of the:

a) hour and minute hands at 10 o'clock

b) minute and second hands 15 seconds before 20 past the hour

So the minute hand is at 19.75 minutes past the hour.

c) hour and minute hands at 1020.

Q13 A surveyor wants to measure the height of a building. She measures the angle of elevation of the top of the building from the two different positions shown. Calculate the height of the building to the nearest metre.

Q14 Mary and Jane were standing one behind the other, 2.3 m apart, each holding one of the two strings of a kite flying directly in front of them. The angles of elevation of the kite from the girls were 65° and 48° respectively. Assuming the ends of both strings are held at the same height above the ground, calculate the length of each string.

UNIT 3 — GEOMETRY AND ALGEBRA

The Graphs of Sin and Cos

Remember — <u>Sin</u> and <u>Cos</u> only have values between <u>–1 and 1</u>.

Q1

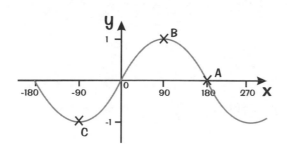

This is the graph of $y = \sin(x)$. Write down the coordinates of the points A, B and C.

Q2

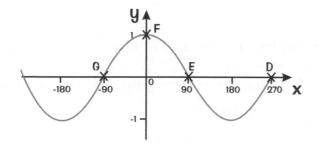

This is the graph of $y = \cos(x)$. Write down the coordinates of the points D, E, F and G.

Q3 Which of the graphs $y = \sin(x)$ or $y = \cos(x)$ go through the points labelled A, B, C, ...J? (Sometimes it is neither.)

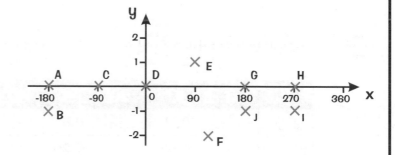

Q4 Plot the points given in this table.

x	0	90	180	270	360
y	2	1	0	1	2

Write down an equation for the curve you have plotted.

Q5 For $0° \leqslant x \leqslant 360°$, draw the curves of:
a) $y = \sin(2x)$
b) $y = 2\sin(2x)$

Careful with these stretches — sin(kx) isn't the same as ksin(x).

The Graphs of Sin and Cos

Q6   Draw the curve of $y = 1 + \cos(x)$ for $-180° \leqslant x \leqslant 180°$

Q7   Draw the curve of $y = -\sin(x)$ for $0° \leqslant x \leqslant 360°$.
What transformation is this of $y = \sin(x)$?

Q8   Draw accurately the graph of $y = 10\cos(x)$ for $-180° \leqslant x \leqslant 180°$.
On the same axes draw the graph of $10y = x + 20$.
Write down the coordinates of where the graphs cross. Show that this can be used to find a solution to the equation:
$$20 = 100\cos(x) - x.$$

Q9   Complete this table of values for $\sin(x)$ and $(\sin(x))^2$.

X	0	10	20	30	40	50	60	70	80	90
sin x		0.17		0.5						1
$(\sin x)^2$		0.03		0.25						1

Draw axes for the graph from $-180° \leqslant x \leqslant 180°$.
Plot the points for $(\sin(x))^2$.
From your knowledge of sin graphs, draw the rest of the graph for the limits given.

Q10   Draw accurately the graph of $y = \sin(x)$ for $0° \leqslant x \leqslant 180°$. Let the y-axis have values -2 to $+2$.
On the same axis, draw the graph of $10y - x = -20$.
Use your graphs to find an approximate solution to the equation $x = 10\sin(x) + 20$.

UNIT 3 — GEOMETRY AND ALGEBRA

Graphs: Shifts and Stretches

You've got to learn the rules for these <u>shifts</u> and <u>stretches</u> — there are <u>only 4</u> types, so it won't take long. If you don't, either you'll have to <u>spend ages</u> working it out, or worse still you'll <u>have to guess</u>. Seems a bit of a waste of time <u>and marks</u> to me...

Q1   This is a graph of $y = f(x)$.

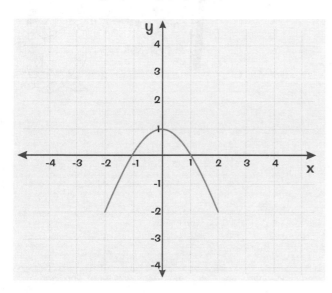

Use the graph of $y = f(x)$ to sketch:

a) $y = f(x) + 3$
b) $y = f(x) - 3$
c) $y = f(x + 3)$
d) $y = f(x - 3)$
e) $y = -f(x)$
f) $y = f(2x)$
g) $y = f(\frac{1}{2}x)$
h) $y = -f(2x)$

Q2   This is a graph of $y = f(x)$.

Use the graph of $y = f(x)$ to sketch:

a) $y = f(x) + 2$
b) $y = f(x) - 2$
c) $y = f(x + 2)$
d) $y = f(x - 2)$
e) $y = -f(x)$
f) $y = f(2x)$
g) $y = f(\frac{1}{2}x)$
h) $y = f(x + 3) - 1$
i) $y = f(x - 1) + 3$

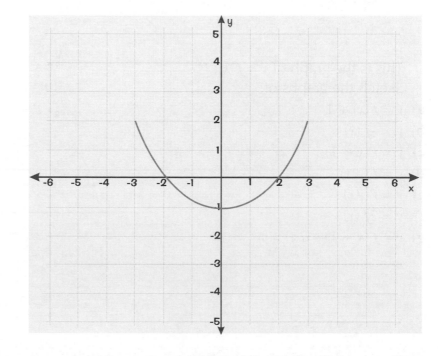

Graphs: Shifts and Stretches

Q3   A sound engineer wants to alter a recorded sound.
He brings up an image of the sound wave on a monitor, as shown below.

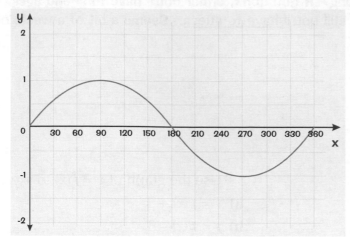

Draw what the engineer will
see on the monitor if the altered
sound wave has the equation:

a) $y = 2\sin(x)$

b) $y = \sin(2x)$.

Q4   This is the graph of $y = \cos(x)$:

Draw the graphs of:

a) $y = 2\cos(x)$

b) $y = \cos(2x)$.

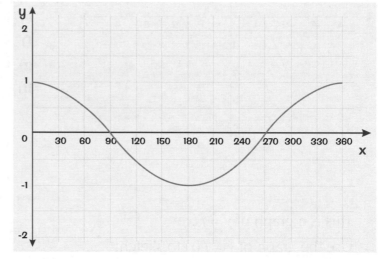

Q5   This is the graph of $y = f(x)$:
Sketch the graphs of:

a) $y = f(x) + 1$

b) $y = -f(x)$

c) $y = f(x + 1)$

d) $y = f(\frac{1}{2}x)$

e) $y = f(2x)$

f) $y = 2f(x)$

g) $y = f(x + 1) - 2$.

Loci and Constructions

Don't let a silly word like <u>locus</u> put you off — there are <u>easy marks</u> to be had here, but you've got to do everything neatly, using a pencil, ruler and compasses.

Q1 Inside a 6 cm by 4 cm rectangle:

a) draw the locus of points 5 cm from D

b) draw the locus of points equidistant from A and D

c) indicate by an X, the point inside the rectangle which is 5 cm from D and equidistant from A and D.

Q2 Use a ruler and protractor to accurately construct triangle PQR with length PQ = 10.5 cm, angle PQR = 95° and angle RPQ = 32°.

a) Construct the perpendicular bisector of the line PR. Draw in point A where the bisector crosses the line PQ.

b) Bisect angle PRQ. Draw in point B where the bisector crosses the line PQ. Measure the length BA.

Q3 Omar is doing some garden landscaping. Because of gas and water pipes, he is not allowed to dig anywhere within 3 m of his house.

Using a scale of 1 cm to 1 m, draw a diagram for Omar showing the walls of his house and the area in which he cannot dig.

UNIT 3 — GEOMETRY AND ALGEBRA

Loci and Constructions

Q4   Use a ruler and protractor to construct triangle PQR
with length PQ = QR = 11.5 cm and angle PQR = 38°.

   a) Construct the bisectors of angles QPR and QRP.
Mark the point O where the 2 bisectors cross.

   b) With centre O draw the circle which just touches
the sides PQ, PR and QR of the triangle.
What is the radius of this circle?

Q5   A and B are 2 points on a straight shore, 4 km apart with A due west of B.

   a) Describe the locus of points P such that angle APB equals 90°.

   b) Using a scale of 2 cm to 1 km draw an accurate scale
diagram showing A, B, the shore line and the locus of P.

*Think about your
geometry rules.*

An outcrop of rock is located on a bearing of 060° from A and 300° from B.

   c) Indicate the rock on your diagram. Mark the spot with an X.

   d) A ship steaming due east parallel to the shore avoids the rock by
following the locus of P. How near does the ship come to the rock?

Q6   This is a plan of Simon's room.

To keep warm Simon must be within 2 m of
the wall with the radiator on. To see out of
the window he must be within 1.5 m of the
wall containing the window.

   a) Using a scale of 2 cm to 1 m draw a plan of
Simon's room.

   b) Shade the region in which Simon must be if
he is to be warm and see out of the window.

Loci and Constructions

Just to be really awkward, these points don't always make a nice line — they can cover a whole area... and you're gonna be asked to shade areas containing all the points.

Q7 A running track is designed so that each point on the track is 32.5 m from a fixed line AB which is 100 m long.

A ——————————— 100 m ——————————— B

a) Draw the locus of the line.

b) Calculate the distance once round the running track.

Q8 Jim is landscaping his back garden, and has drawn the plan below. Two sides of the garden are bounded by fences and the other sides are bounded by the walls of the house and garage. The garden is in the shape of a rectangle.

a) Using a scale of 1 cm to 1 m draw a plan of Jim's garden.

b) Ben, the family dog, will be tethered to the garage at B by a lead of length 6 m. Construct accurately and shade the part of the garden where Ben can go.

c) Jim wants to plant a tree in the garden. The tree must be planted more than 5 m away from the wall of the house and more than 4 m away from each fence. It must also be out of reach of Ben, and be more than 2 m away from the wall of the garage. On your plan of the garden, construct accurately and shade the region where Jim can plant his tree.

Q9 The positions of two islands A and B are found from the following information: A is 35 km from a jetty J on a bearing 065°, B is due south of A and on a bearing of 132° from J as shown below.

a) Using a scale of 1 cm to 5 km, draw an accurate plan to show the positions of J, A and B.

b) Find from your drawing the distance in km between the islands A and B.

c) A boat leaves the jetty at 09.00 and reaches A at 11.30. What is its average speed in km/h?

d) A lightship L is 20 km from J, equidistant from A and B and on the same side of J as A and B. Mark L on the drawing.

e) Find the bearing of L from J.

Conversion Factors and Metric & Imperial Units

You've got to know all the metric and imperial conversion factors — there's no way out of it, you'll just have to sit down and learn them, sorry and all that...

Q1 Express the given quantity in the unit(s) in brackets:

a) 2 m [cm]
b) 3.3 cm [mm]
c) 4 kg [g]
d) 600 g [kg]
e) 4 ft [in]
f) 36 in [ft]
g) 87 in [ft and in]

h) 43 oz [lb and oz]
i) 650 m [km]
j) 9 kg [g]
k) 7 g [kg]
l) 950 g [kg]
m) 6 ft [in]
n) 5 lb [oz]

o) 301 ft [yd and ft]
p) 6 m [mm]
q) 2 tonnes [kg]
r) 3000 g [kg]
s) 8 cm 6 mm [mm]
t) 3 ft 6 in [in]
u) 4 lb 7 oz [oz]

v) 550 kg [tonnes]
w) 3 m 54 cm [cm]
x) 0.7 cm [mm]

Q2 Convert 147 kg into pounds.

Q3 A horse's drinking trough holds 14 gallons of water. Approximately how many litres is this?

Q4 Deborah is filling in a health questionnaire. She needs to write down her weight in kilograms. She weighs 9 stone 4 pounds. There are 14 pounds in a stone and 1 kilogram is equal to 0.157 stone. How much does Deborah weigh in kilograms?

Q5 Barbara cycled 51 km in one day while Barry cycled 30 miles. Who cycled further?

Q6 A seamstress needs to cut an 11 inch strip of finest Chinese silk.
a) Approximately how many cm is this?
b) Approximately how many mm is this?

Q7 The priceless Greek statue in my garden is 750 cm tall.
a) How many inches is this?
b) How many metres is this?
c) How many mm is this?
d) How many km is this?

Q8 Dick is making The World's Wobbliest Jelly. The recipe requires 5 lb of sugar. How many 1 kg bags of sugar does Dick need to buy so that he can make the jelly?

Q9 The Bon Voyage Holiday Company are offering an exchange rate of 1.48 euros for £1 sterling. They are also offering 11.03 Danish kroner for £1 sterling and 2.45 Australian dollars for £1 sterling. Calculate, to the nearest penny, the sterling equivalent of:
a) 220 euros
b) 686 Danish kroner
c) 1664 Australian dollars
d) 148 euros
e) 15 Danish kroner
f) 1950 Australian dollars
g) 899 Danish kroner
h) 20 euros
i) 668 Australian dollars
j) 3389 Danish kroner
k) 1000 Australian dollars
l) 1 euro

Conversion Factors and Metric & Imperial Units

Q10 At the gym Arnold can lift a barbell weighing 60 kg.
a) Approximately how many lbs is this?
b) How many ounces is this?
Sylvester can lift a barbell weighing 0.059 tonnes.
c) Who can lift the most?

Q11 The scale on a map is 1:10 000.
How big are the following in real life:
a) a distance of 2 cm on the map
b) a distance of 20 cm on the map
c) a distance of 70 cm on the map
d) an area of 2 cm² on the map?

Maps can be tricky. Best thing is to keep the units
the same when you do the initial conversion, then do
another conversion to the appropriate units.

Q12 Another map has a scale of 1:3000.
What size on this map are the following:
a) a distance of 5 km in real life
b) a distance of 1 km in real life
c) an area of 100 m² in real life
d) an area of 50 m² in real life?

Just remember — the distance on the map is
unlikely to be larger than the real-life distance.

Q13 Justin is shopping online. He looks up the following exchange rates:

1.60 US Dollars ($) to £1 Sterling.

150 Japanese Yen (¥) to £1 Sterling.

Calculate to the nearest penny the cost in Sterling of each of Justin's purchases:
a) A book costing $7.50
b) An MP3 player costing ¥7660

Q14 Simon is on holiday in Cyprus. He wants to compare the price of beer there
with the price he pays at home. He knows the following conversion rates.

£1 = €1.15   1 pint = 0.568 litres

A pint of beer in his local pub costs £2.15.
A litre of beer in the poolside bar at his hotel costs €4.00.
Which is better value?

Q15 Neil is going to buy some fabric for a new pair of trousers that he is
going to make. A local shop prices the fabric that he would like at
£9.84 per square yard. A fabric superstore prices the same fabric at
£10.80 per square metre. According to price, where should Neil
buy his fabric? (Use the conversion factor 91 cm = 1 yard.)

UNIT 3 — GEOMETRY AND ALGEBRA

Conversion Factors and Metric & Imperial Units

There's a button on your calculator for this time conversion stuff, by the way...
So get some practice at using it before the exam.

Q16 The times below are given using a 24 hour system. Using am or pm, give the equivalent time for a 12 hour clock.

a) 0500　　　　　　c) 0316　　　　　　e) 2230

b) 1448　　　　　　d) 1558　　　　　　f) 0001

Q17 The times below are taken from a 12 hour clock. Give the equivalent 24 hour readings.

a) 11.30 pm　　　　c) 12.15 am　　　　e) 8.30 am

b) 10.22 am　　　　d) 12.15 pm　　　　f) 4.45 pm

Q18 Joe is watching a film. It starts at 19.55 and ends at 22.20.
How many minutes does the film last?

Q19 Find the time elapsed between the following pairs of times:

a) 0820 on 1 October 2010 and 1620 on the same day

b) 10.22 pm on 1 October 2010 and 8.22 am the next day

c) 2.18 am on 1 October 2010 and 2.14 pm later the same day

d) 0310 on 1 October 2010 and 0258 on 3 October 2010.

Q20 Convert the following into hours and minutes:

a) 3.25 hours　　b) 0.4 hours　　c) 7.3 hours　　d) 1.2 hours.

Q21 Convert the following into just hours:

a) 2 hours and 20 minutes

b) 3 hours and 6 minutes

c) 20 minutes.

Formula Triangles

This is what you've been waiting for — perhaps the <u>most important page</u> in this section. Get the hang of this bit and you can use it to help you with <u>anything</u>... well, nearly.

> You can use a formula triangle for **<u>ANY FORMULA</u>** with **<u>THREE THINGS</u>**, where two are **<u>MULTIPLIED</u>** to give the third.

E.g. area of a rectangle = length × height.
This will give the formula triangle:

All you do is cover up what you want with your finger and the other two bits will tell you how to calculate it. Couldn't be simpler.

Q1 The formula for finding the area of a triangle is Area = half base × height, i.e. $A = \left(\frac{b}{2}\right) \times h$. Draw a <u>formula triangle</u> and use it to find:

a) the area of triangle A
b) the height of triangle B given that its area is 26 cm²
c) the base length of triangle C with area 49 cm².

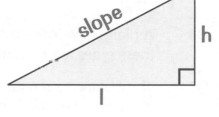

Q2 The <u>gradient</u> of a slope is found by dividing the height by the length, $g = \frac{h}{l}$. Draw a formula triangle and use it to find:

a) the gradient of a hill that rises 2 m for each 10 m in length
b) the height a road has risen for 18 m horizontally if the gradient is $\frac{1}{6}$.
c) how much horizontal space a children's slide will take up if it is 3 m high and has a gradient of $\frac{2}{3}$.

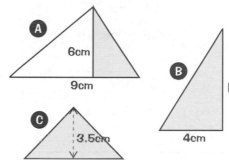

Q3 The <u>circumference of a circle</u> is given by the formula $c = \pi d$, c = circumference, d = diameter. Draw a formula triangle and use it to find:
a) the circumference of a bike wheel with a diameter of 72 cm
b) the diameter of a jam jar with a circumference of 21 cm
c) the length of string needed which, when swung in a circle, makes a circumference of 250 cm.

Q4 A formula used by accountants is $L = S/Q$. L is Lateral Forecast, S is the Spend Parameter and Q is the Quotient Charter. Draw a formula triangle relating L, S and Q and use it to find:
a) the Lateral Forecast when the Spend Parameter is 120 and the Quotient Charter is 8
b) the Quotient Charter when the Spend Parameter is 408 whilst the Lateral Forecast is 24
c) S when $L = 0$.

UNIT 3 — GEOMETRY AND ALGEBRA

Speed, Distance and Time

This is an easy enough formula — and of course you can put it in that good old formula triangle as well.

$$\text{Average speed} = \frac{\text{Total distance}}{\text{Total time}}$$

Q1 A train travels 240 km in 4 hours. What is its <u>average speed</u>?

Q2 A car travels for 3 hours at an average speed of 55 mph. How far has it travelled?

Q3 A boy rides a bike at an average speed of 15 km/h. How long will it take him to ride 40 km?

Q4 <u>Complete</u> this table.

Distance Travelled	Time taken	Average Speed
210 km	3 hrs	
135 miles		30 mph
	2 hrs 30 mins	42 km/h
9 miles	45 mins	
640 km		800 km/h
	1 hr 10 mins	60 mph

Q5 An athlete can run 100 m in 11 seconds.
Calculate the athlete's speed in:
a) m/s
b) km/h.

Q6 A plane flies over city A at 09.55 and over city B at 10.02. What is its <u>average</u> speed if these cities are 63 miles apart?

Q7 The distance from Kendal (Oxenholme) to London (Euston) is 260 miles. The train travels at an average speed of 71 mph. Pete needs to be in London by 10.30. If he catches the 07.05 from Kendal, will he be in London on time? <u>Show all your working</u>.

Q8 In a speed trial a sand yacht travelled a measured mile in 36.4 seconds.
a) Calculate this speed in mph.
On the return mile he took 36.16 seconds.
b) Find his <u>total time</u> for the two runs.
c) Calculate the average speed of the two runs in mph.

Remember, for the <u>average</u> speed, you use the <u>total</u> time and <u>total</u> distance.

Q9 A motorist drives from Manchester to London. 180 miles is on motorway where he averages 65 mph. 55 miles is on city roads where he averages 28 mph, 15 miles is on country roads where he averages 25 mph.
a) Calculate the total time taken for the journey.
b) How far did he travel altogether?
c) Calculate the average speed for the journey.

Speed, Distance and Time

Q10 Victor walks at an average speed of 4 km/h. He needs to walk to Askam-in-Furness, 3 km away. He needs to be there at 3.00pm. What time should he set off?

Q11 The distance between two railway stations is 145 km.
a) How long does a train travelling at 65 km/h on average take to travel this distance?
b) Another train travels at an average speed of 80 km/h but has a 10 min stop during the journey. How long does this second train take?
c) If both arrive at 1600, what time did each leave?

Q12 Two athletes run a road race. One ran at an average speed of 16 km/h, the other at 4 m/s. Which was the fastest? How long would each take to run 10 km?

Q13 A plane leaves Amsterdam at 0715 and flies at an average speed of 650 km/h to Paris, arriving at 0800. It takes off again at 0840 and flies at the same average speed to Nice arriving at 1005.
a) How far is it from Amsterdam to Paris?
b) How far is it from Paris to Nice?
c) What was the average speed for the whole journey?

Q14 A runner covered the first 100 m of a 200 m race in 12.3 seconds.
a) What was his average speed for the first 100 m?
b) The second 100 m took 15.1 seconds. What was his average speed for the 200 m?

Q15 A military plane can achieve a speed of 1100 km/h. At this speed it passes over town A at 1205 and town B at 1217.
a) How far apart are towns A and B?
b) The plane then flies over village C which is 93 km from B. How long does it take from B to C?

Q16 Two cars set off on 180 mile journeys. One travels mostly on A roads and manages an average speed of 42 mph. The other car travels mostly on the motorway and achieves an average speed of 64 mph. If they both take the same time over the journey, for how long does the second car stop?

Q17 A stone is dropped from a cliff top. After 1 second it has fallen 4.8 m, after 2 seconds a total of 19.2 m and after 3 seconds 43.2 m. Calculate its average speed in:
a) the first second
b) the second second
c) for all 3 seconds
d) Change all the m/s speeds to km/h.

Q18 In 1990 three motor racers had fastest lap speeds of 236.6, 233.8 and 227.3 km/h. If 1 km = 0.62 miles, how long would each driver take to lap 5 miles at these speeds?

128

Density

Here we go again — the multi-purpose formula triangle. Learn the positions of M, D and V, plug in the numbers and pull out the answer... magic.

$$\text{DENSITY} = \frac{\text{mass}}{\text{volume}}$$

Q1 Find the <u>density</u> of each of these pieces of wood, giving your answer in g/cm³:

a) Mass 3 g, volume 4 cm³
b) Mass 12 kg, volume 20,000 cm³
c) Mass 20 g, volume 25 cm³
d) Mass 14 kg, volume 0.02 m³.

Q2 Calculate the <u>mass</u> of each of these objects:

a) a small marble statue of density 2.6 g/cm³ and volume 24 cm³
b) a plastic cube of volume 64 cm³ and density 1.5 g/cm³
c) a gold ingot measuring 12 cm by 4 cm by 4 cm with density 19.5 g/cm³
d) a pebble with volume 30 cm³ and density 2.5 g/cm³.

Q3 Work out the <u>volume</u> of each of these items:
a) a bag of sugar of mass 1 kg and density 1.6 g/cm³
b) a packet of margarine with density 2.8 g/cm³ and mass 250 g
c) a 50 kg sack of coal with density 1.8 g/cm³
d) a box of cereal with density 0.2 g/cm³ and mass 500 g.

Q4 My copper bracelet has a volume of 3.9 cm³. The density of copper is 8.9 g/cm³. Work out the <u>mass</u> of my bracelet.

Q5 Ice has a density of 0.93 g/cm³. If the mass of a block of ice is 19.5 kg, what is its <u>volume</u>?

Q6 Some petrol in a can has a mass of 4 kg. The density of the petrol is 0.8 g/cm³. How many <u>litres</u> of petrol are in the can?

1 litre = 1000 cm³.

Q7 A jug holds 1.9 litres of lemonade. The mass of the lemonade is 2 kg. Find the <u>density</u> of the lemonade.

Q8 A 1.5 kg bag full of self raising flour measures 12 cm by 18 cm by 6 cm. A 1 kg bag of granary flour measures 10 cm by 14 cm by 6 cm.
a) Find the <u>density</u> of each sort of flour.
b) Jake needs to measure out 450 g of granary flour but his scales are broken. Use your answer to part **a)** to work out how much flour he should measure out in his measuring jug. Give your answer in ml.

1 ml = 1 cm³

UNIT 3 — GEOMETRY AND ALGEBRA

Estimating

Q1 Without using your calculator find approximate answers to the following:

a) 6560 × 1.97   g) 7139 × 2.13

b) 8091 × 1.456   h) 98 × 2.54 × 2.033

c) 38.45 × 1.4237 × 5.0002   i) 21 × 21 × 21

d) 45.34 ÷ 9.345   j) 8143 ÷ 81

e) 34504 ÷ 7133   k) 62000 ÷ 950

f) $\dfrac{55.33 \times 19.345}{9.23}$ l) $\pi \div 3$

Turn these into nice easy numbers that you can deal with without a calculator.

Q2 At the start of the week, a shop had approximately 15 000 cartons of broccoli juice in stock. The shop sold 1483 cartons on Monday, 2649 on Tuesday, 1539 on Wednesday, 1478 on Thursday and 2958 on Friday. Estimate the number of cartons remaining.

Q3 Estimate the area under the graph.

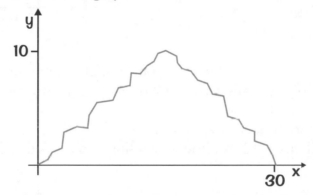

Q4 A supermarket chain sold 14634 tins of beans during a four week period.

a) If the supermarkets were open every day of the week, how many days did it take to sell the 14634 tins of beans?

b) What was the average number of tins of beans sold each day?

c) Show your working for a rough estimate to **b)** to check that your answer is of the right order of magnitude.

"of the right order of magnitude" is just a posh way to say "the right size", by the way.

Q5 π is the number of times that the diameter of a circle divides into the circumference. Many values have been used as estimates — here are a few examples:
$$3, \ \frac{22}{7}, \ \sqrt{10}, \ \frac{255}{81}, \ 3\frac{17}{120}.$$

a) Use your calculator to give each estimate correct to 7 decimal places.

b) Which is the most accurate estimate for π?

Estimating

Q6 Showing all your working, estimate the value of the following:

a) $\dfrac{144.5 + 49.1}{153.2 - 41.2}$

b) $\dfrac{18.2 \times 10.7}{\sqrt{398.6}}$

c) $\dfrac{2021.23 \times 4.0436}{20.33 \times 4.902}$

d) $\dfrac{(9.2)^2 \div 10.3}{4.306 \times 5.011}$

Q7 Estimate the areas of the following:

a)

44.3cm

26.4cm

b)

3.89km

5.2km

Q8 Joan needs to estimate the size of her bedroom so that she can buy enough paint to cover the walls. Two of the walls measure 2.86 m by 3.16 m, and the other two walls measure 2.86 m by 3.42 m.

a) Estimate the area that Joan needs to paint in m².

b) If one tin of paint will cover 15 m², how many tins of paint will Joan need to paint her bedroom?

Q9 Estimate these volumes:

a)

4cm

9.7cm

3.1cm

b)

10cm

22.3cm

Q10 Mark wants to buy some tropical fish.
The pet shop owner tells him that he will need a tank with a volume of at least 7000 cm³.
Estimate whether Mark's tank will be big enough.

10.4 cm

29.6 cm

14.8 cm

Vectors

Q1 ABCDE is a pentagon.

$$\vec{AB} = \begin{pmatrix} 3 \\ 3 \end{pmatrix} \quad \vec{AC} = \begin{pmatrix} 2 \\ 6 \end{pmatrix} \quad \vec{AD} = \begin{pmatrix} -2 \\ 6 \end{pmatrix} \quad \vec{AE} = \begin{pmatrix} -3 \\ 2 \end{pmatrix}$$

a) Draw this pentagon accurately.

b) Write down the vectors:

   i) $\vec{DE}$ **ii)** $\vec{DC}$ **iii)** $\vec{EC}$

c) What sort of triangle is $\triangle$ ACD?

Q2 $\underset{\sim}{p} = \begin{pmatrix} 2 \\ 3 \end{pmatrix},\ \underset{\sim}{q} = \begin{pmatrix} 0 \\ -2 \end{pmatrix},\ \underset{\sim}{r} = \begin{pmatrix} 3 \\ -1 \end{pmatrix},\ \underset{\sim}{s} = \begin{pmatrix} -1 \\ -2 \end{pmatrix}$

Calculate then draw:

a) $\underset{\sim}{p} + \underset{\sim}{q}$ **c)** $2\underset{\sim}{r}$ **e)** $2\underset{\sim}{p} - 2\underset{\sim}{s}$ **g)** $2\underset{\sim}{r} - \underset{\sim}{q}$ **i)** $\underset{\sim}{p} + 2\underset{\sim}{s}$

b) $\underset{\sim}{p} - \underset{\sim}{q}$ **d)** $\underset{\sim}{s} + \underset{\sim}{p}$ **f)** $3\underset{\sim}{q} + \underset{\sim}{s}$ **h)** $\frac{1}{2}\underset{\sim}{q} + 2\underset{\sim}{r}$ **j)** $\underset{\sim}{q} - 2\underset{\sim}{r}$

Q3

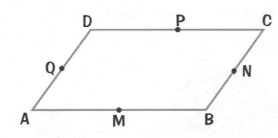

ABCD is a parallelogram. M, N, P and Q are the mid-points of the sides, as shown.
$\vec{MQ} = \underset{\sim}{x}$ and $\vec{AM} = \underset{\sim}{y}$.

Express in terms of $\underset{\sim}{x}$ and $\underset{\sim}{y}$:

a) $\vec{AB}$ **c)** $\vec{NB}$ **e)** $\vec{AC}$

b) $\vec{AQ}$ **d)** $\vec{BC}$ **f)** $\vec{BD}$

Q4 In the diagram on the right, EB and AC are perpendicular. ABCE is a parallelogram. $\angle$EDC is a right angle.

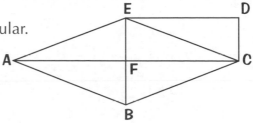

a) Name a vector equal to:

   i) $\vec{FC}$ **iii)** $\vec{BC}$ **v)** $2\vec{CD}$ **vii)** $\vec{EF} - \vec{CF}$

   ii) $\vec{FB}$ **iv)** $\vec{CE}$ **vi)** $\vec{AE} + \vec{EC}$ **viii)** $\vec{ED} + \vec{DC} + \vec{CB}$

b) If AC = 16 cm and EB = 6 cm:
   i) what is the area of ABCE?
   ii) what is the area of ABCDE?

Real-Life Vectors

Look at the pretty pictures... make sure you can see how this little lot fit with the questions.

Q1 In still water my motor boat can achieve 9 km/h. I aim the boat directly across the river which is running at 3 km/h. What is my resultant speed?

Q2

Casey is taking part in a swimming race across a river. The river flows at 2 km/h. Casey can swim at 3.5 km/h.

a) What angle to the bank should she swim to go directly across the river and have the best chance of winning?

b) Calculate her resultant speed.

Q3 An aircraft is attempting to fly due north. The plane travels at 600 km/h, but the pilot has to compensate for a strong 75 km/h wind from the west, as shown.

a) What bearing should the pilot fly the plane on to avoid being blown off course?

b) Calculate the aircraft's resultant speed.

Remember — bearings are measured clockwise from the north line.

Q4 In the following diagrams, forces are acting on an object as shown.

i) 10 N, 12 N

ii) 10 N, 15 N

iii) 23N, 20N

For each find:

a) the resultant force

b) its direction in relation to the larger force.

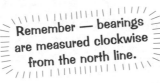

Put the vectors end to end and complete the triangle.

UNIT 3 — GEOMETRY AND ALGEBRA

Answers

Contents

Answers: P.1 — P.10

Unit 1 — Statistics and Number

Rounding Numbers P.1-P.2

Q1 a) 62.2   b) 62.19
c) 62.194   d) 19.62433
e) 6.300   f) 3.142

Q2 a) 1330   b) 1330
c) 1329.6   d) 100
e) 0.02   f) 0.02469

Q3 a) 457.0   b) 456.99
c) 456.987   d) 457
e) 460   f) 500

Q4 2.83

Q5 a) 0.704 (to 3 s.f. — the least number of significant figures used in the question).
b) 3.25 (to 3 s.f. — the least number of significant figures used in the question).

Q6 23 kg

Q7 £5.07

Q8 235 miles

Q9 £19

Q10 £4.77

Q11 235 cm

Q12 4.5 m to 5.5 m

Q13 a) 142.465 kg
b) 142.455 kg

Q14 a) Perimeter = 2(12 + 4) = 32 cm.
Maximum possible error = 4 × 0.1 cm = 0.4 cm.
b) Maximum possible error in P is 2($x + y$).

Rounding and Accuracy P.3

Q1 a) 807.87 m^2
b) 808 m^2
c) Answer b) is more reasonable.

Q2 a) 80872 kg   b) 3.9 miles
c) 1.56 m   d) 150 kg
e) 6 buses   f) 12 ºC

Q3 a) 43 g   b) 7.22 m
c) 3.429 g   d) 1.1 litres
e) 0.54 (or 0.5) miles
f) 28.4 miles per gallon

Q4 a) 0.721 (to 3 sf)
b) 3.73 (to 3 sf)

Calculation Bounds P.4-P.5

Q1 a) 64.785 kg   b) 64.775 kg

Q2 a) 1.75 m
b) 1.85 × 0.75 = 1.3875 m^2

Q3 13.75 kg

Q4 a) 95 g
b) Upper bound = 97.5 g, lower bound = 92.5 g.
c) No, since the lower bound for the electronic scales is 97.5 g, which is greater than the upper bound for the scales in part a).

Q5 a) Upper bound = 945, lower bound = 935.
b) Upper bound = 5.565, lower bound = 5.555.

c) To find the upper bound for R, divide the upper bound for S by the lower bound for T;
945 ÷ 5.555 = 170.117...
To find the lower bound for R, divide the lower bound for S by the upper bound for T;
935÷5.565 = 168.014...
d) 940÷5.56 = 170 (to 2 s.f. — the upper and lower bounds both round to 170 to 2 s.f., but give different answers to 3 s.f.).

Q6 a) Upper bound = 13.5, lower bound = 12.5.
b) Upper bound = 12.55, lower bound = 12.45.
c) To calculate the upper bound for C multiply the upper bound for A by the upper bound for B;
13.5×12.55 = 169.425
To calculate the lower bound for C multiply the lower bound for A by the lower bound for B;
12.5×12.45 = 155.625

Q7 At least 18.2 m^2

Q8 The upper bound for the distance is 100.5 m. The lower bound for the time is 10.25 s. Therefore the maximum value of Vince's average speed is 100.5÷10.25 = 9.805 m/s.

Q9 The upper bound for the distance is 127.5 km. The lower bound for the time is 1 hour and 45 minutes = 1.75 hours. The maximum value of the average speed is 127.5÷1.75 = 72.857... km/hour.

Q10 a) Upper bound = 5 minutes 32.5 seconds, lower bound = 5 minutes 27.5 seconds.
b) The lower bound for Jimmy's time is 5 minutes 25 seconds, which is lower than the lower bound for Douglas' time (5 minutes 25.5 seconds).

Standard Index Form P.6-P.7

Q1 a) 35.6   b) 3560
c) 0.356   d) 35600
e) 8.2   f) 0.00082
g) 0.82   h) 0.0082
i) 1570   j) 0.157
k) 157000   l) 15.7

Q2 a) 2.56×10^0 b) 2.56×10
c) 2.56×10^{-1} d) 2.56×10^4
e) 9.52×10 f) 9.52×10^{-2}
g) 9.52×10^4 h) 9.52×10^{-4}
i) 4.2×10^3 j) 4.2×10^{-3}
k) 4.2×10 l) 4.2×10^2

Q3 a) 3.47×10^7 b) 7.3004×10
c) 5×10^0 d) 9.183×10^5
e) 1.5×10^7 f) 9.371×10^6
g) 7.5×10^{-5} h) 5×10^{-4}
i) 5.34×10^0 j) 6.2103×10^2
k) 1.49×10^4 l) 3×10^{-7}

Q4 6×10^{-3}

Q5 1×10^9, 1×10^{12}

Q6 9.46×10^{12}

Q7 6.9138×10^4

Q8 1.2×10^{-2} (mm)

Q9 a) Mercury   b) Jupiter
c) Mercury   d) Neptune

e) Venus and Mercury
f) Jupiter, Neptune and Saturn

Q10 a) 2.4×10^{10}
b) 1.6×10^6
c) 1.8×10^5

Q11 1.04×10^{13} is greater by 5.78×10^{12}

Q12 1.3×10^{-9} is smaller by 3.07×10^{-8}

Q13 a) 4.2×10^7 b) 3.8×10^{-4}
c) 1.0×10^7 d) 1.12×10^{-4}
e) 8.43×10^5 f) 4.232×10^{-3}
g) 1.7×10^{18} h) 2.83×10^{-4}
i) 1×10^{-2}

Q14 7×10^6

Q15 6.38×10^8 cm

Q16 3.322×10^{-27} kg

Q17 a) 1.8922×10^{16} m
b) 4.7305×10^{15} m

Q18 a) 510000000 km^2
b) 3.62×10^8 km^2
c) 148000000 km^2

Calculator Buttons P.8-P.9

Q1 a) 1   f) 900
b) 4   g) 25
c) 121   h) 1 000 000
d) 256   i) 0
e) 1

Q2 a) 4   f) 20
b) 6   g) 1.732 (to 3 d.p.)
c) 17   h) 2.646 (to 3 d.p.)
d) 0   i) 5.477 (to 3 d.p.)
e) 60

Q3 a) 1   e) 3
b) 0   f) −3
c) 7   g) −4
d) 10   h) −1.710 (to 3 d.p.)

Q4 a) 8.4   d) 3.403 (3 d.p)
b) 0.00172 (3 s.f.)   e) 0.874 (3 d.p)
c) 0.656 (3 d.p)   f) 1.174 (3 d.p)

Q5 a) 2   d) 29.867 (3 d.p.)
b) 1   e) 0.353 (3 d.p.)
c) 0.333 (3 d.p.)   f) 0.0729 (3 s.f.)

Q6 a) 1   f) 59 049
b) 1 048 576   g) 0.487 (3 d.p.)
c) 1 048 576   h) 26 742 (5 s.f.)
d) 9.870 (3 d.p.)   i) 0.25
e) 0.5

Q7 a) 4.5×10^3 b) 9.5×10^3
c) 5.793×10^6 d) 4.5×10^{15}
e) 1.8704×10^7 f) 1.168×10^{11}

Q8 a) 4   d) 0.05
b) 0.2   e) 0.02
c) 2   f) 400

Fractions With a Calculator P.10

Q1 a) $\frac{1}{18}$ b) $\frac{1}{4}$

Q2 a) 48 km^2 b) $\frac{5}{8}$

Q3 a) 8 people   b) $\frac{7}{20}$

c) $\frac{1}{4}$ d) 57 people

e) 65 people

Answers: P.11 — P.19

Q4 After the 1st bounce the ball reaches 4 m, after the 2nd $2\frac{2}{3}$ m, after the 3rd $1\frac{7}{9}$ m.

Q5 a) 100 g flour   b) 350 g

     c) $\frac{2}{7}$ d) 300 g

Q6 £31.06

Percentages P.11-P.13

Q1 a) 0.2   c) 0.02
     b) 0.35   d) 0.625

Q2 a) $\frac{1}{5}$ c) $\frac{7}{10}$

     b) $\frac{3}{100}$ d) $\frac{421}{500}$

Q3 a) 12.5%   c) 30%
     b) 23%   d) 34%

Q4 85%

Q5 72.5%

Q6 £351.33

Q7 £244.40

Q8 23 028

Q9 a) £4275   b) £6840

Q10 Car 1 costs £8495 − (0.15 × £8495)
= £8495 − £1274.25 = £7220.75.
Car 2 costs £8195 − (0.12 × £8195)
= £8195 − £983.40 = £7211.60.
So car 2 is the cheapest.

Q11 a) £5980   b) £5501.60

Q12 £152.75, So NO, he couldn't afford it.

Q13 31%

Q14 13%

Q15 1.6%

Q16 500%

Q17 a) 67.7%
     b) 93.5%
     c) 38.1%

Q18 a) £236.25
     b) £1000 × 1.07³ − £1000 = £225.04
     c) £1000 × 1.07875³ − £1000 = £255.34

Q19 38%

Q20 £80

Q21 a) 300
     b) 4 whole years

Compound Growth and Decay P.14-P.15

Q1 a) £473.47   c) £909.12
     b) £612.52   d) £1081.90

Q2 a) 281
     b) 3036
     c) 27 hours

Q3 a) 8.214 kg   c) 7.272 kg
     b) 7.497 kg   d) 3.836 kg

Q4 a) £1920.80   c) £434.06
     b) £27 671.04   d) £34 974.86

Q5 Second option by £2.20

Q6 £462.08

Q7 £3162.91

Q8 a) 910.91
     b) 754.32

---

c) 114.39
d) about 30 hours

Q9 a) £7877.94   d) £10 646.54
     b) £27,116.06   e) £7184.25
     c) £9980.90   f) £5843.70

Q10 a) £128 606
     b) £103 788
     c) £77 974
     d) £475 000

Q11 a) 51
     b) 52
     c) 50
     d) 61

Q12 a) 16.85 million
     b) 20.72 million

Ratios P.16

Q1 a) 3:4   d) 9:16
     b) 1:4   e) 7:2
     c) 1:2   f) 9:1

Q2 a) 6 cm   d) 1.5 cm
     b) 11 cm   e) 2.75 cm
     c) 30.4 m   f) 7.6 m

Q3 30

Q4 a) 250/500 = 1/2
     b) 150/500 = 3/10

Q5 a) 1:300
     b) 6 m
     c) 3.3 cm

Q6 a) 210 boys   b) 455 pupils

Q7 a) 30 fine
     b) 15 not fine
     c) 30/45 = 2/3

Collecting Data P.17-P.18

Q1 a) Secondary data is data collected by someone else.
     b) Primary data

Q2 a) Secondary data.
     b) Primary data.
     c) Secondary data.

Q3 a) Qualitative
     b) Quantitative
     c) Quantitative
     d) Qualitative

Q4 a) Discrete
     b) Continuous
     c) Discrete
     d) Continuous

Q5 The local council need to know the time of any road traffic accidents that happen at that junction.

Q6 a)

Length of time (mins)	1-10	11-20	21-30	31-40	41-60
Number of people	5	10	5	5	5

     b) You lose some of the accuracy in the data.

Q7 a) The question is subjective – "very often" can mean different things to different people.

---

b) Any sensible answer, e.g. "How many times a week do you visit the school canteen?"

Q8 a) The question is ambiguous because the age classes overlap, e.g. someone who's 30 could go in either the 18-30 or 30-40 group.
     b) Change the answers to:
       "i)   Under 18
       ii)   18 to 30
       iii)   31 to 40
       iv)   41 to 60
       v)   over 60".

Q9 a) Unsuitable — e.g. people may like every one of the desserts, and this wouldn't tell you which was their favourite.
     b) Unsuitable — e.g. the question is not relevant.
     c) Suitable — it is the only one which will always tell you which of the five desserts people like the most.
     d) Unsuitable — e.g. question is too vague, so people may give answers which are not on the list of desserts.
     e) Unsuitable — e.g. people's favourite dessert may not be on the list, so you wouldn't find out which they prefer out of the desserts on the list.

Q10 a) E.g.:

> **Café Questionnaire**
> 1) Please tick the box to show how often you visit the café:
> daily ☐ weekly ☐ fortnightly ☐ monthly ☐ less than monthly ☐
> 2) Please tick the box to show how often you buy cola:
> daily ☐ weekly ☐ fortnightly ☐ monthly ☐ less than monthly ☐

     b) She will miss out the people who just buy drinks from the hot and cold drinks machines.

Sampling P.19

Q1 a) All the moorland dung beetles in the UK
     b) Because it would be extremely difficult and impractical for him to be sure that he had investigated every single moorland dung beetle in the UK.

Q2 a) So that each year group's representation in the sample is proportional to the size of the year.
     b) Total number of students = 1600. (398 ÷ 1600) × 40 = 9.95
Rounded to the nearest person there would be 10 Year 7 students in the sample.
     c) The proportion of Year 11 students is 199/1600, which is roughly 1/8. As we know there are 10 Year 11's in the sample, the group must be 80 pupils.

Q3 a) Do you play any team sports outside school?
Do you take part in any individual sports outside school?
Do you do any exercise at all outside school?
     b) Pick at random 15 girls and 15 boys from each year.

Q4 a) People in a newsagents are likely to be there to buy a newspaper.

UNIT 1 — STATISTICS AND NUMBER

b) At that time on a Sunday, people who go to church are likely to be at church.

c) The bridge club is unlikely to be representative of the population as a whole.

Mean, Median, Mode, Range
P.20-P.21

Q1 3 tries

Q2 mean = 1.333 (to 3 d.p.)
median = 1.5
mode = 2
range = ·11

Q3 **a)** mean = £12,944, or £13,000 to the nearest £500
median = £12,000
mode = £7,500

b) mode

c) E.g. mean — they should use the highest value to attract people to the job.

Q4 **a)** 0 minutes
b) 0 minutes
c) 0 minutes
d) No, according to the raw data.

Q5 73.5 kg

Q6 20 kg

Q7 97%

Q8 **a)** 22 **b)** 74

Q9 **a)** 3.5 **b)** 3.5
c) 5

Q10 **a)** Both spend a mean of 2 hours.
b) The range for Jim is 3 hours and for Bob is 2 hours.
c) The amount of TV that Jim watches each night is more variable than the amount that Bob watches.

Q11 **a)** 1 day **b)** 2 days
c) The statement is true according to the data.

Q12 **a)** mode **b)** median
c) mean

Frequency Tables P.22-P.23

Q1 **a)** 12 **b)** 12

Q2 **a)**

Subject	M	E	F	A	S
Frequency	5	7	3	4	6

b) 36 French lessons
c) English

Q3

Length (m)	4 and under	6	8	10	12	14 and over
Frequency	3	5	6	4	1	1

a) 8 m
b) 8 m **c)** 14 m

Q4

Weight (kg)	Frequency	Weight × Frequency
51	40	2040
52	30	1560
53	45	2385
54	10	540
55	5	275

a) 52 kg
b) 53 kg
c) 52 kg (to nearest kg)

Q5 mean = 3.55
mode = 3
lower quartile = 3
upper quartile = 5
median = 3

Q6 **a)** 4 **c)** 3.2 (to 1 d.p.)
b) 3

Q7 **a) i)** False, mode is 8.
ii) False, they are equal.
iii) True
b) iv)

Grouped Frequency Tables P.24

Q1 **a)**

Speed (km/h)	40≤s<45	45≤s<50	50≤s<55	55≤s<60	60≤s<65
Frequency	4	8	10	7	3
Mid-Interval	42.5	47.5	52.5	57.5	62.5
Frequency × Mid-Interval	170	380	525	402.5	187.5

Estimated mean = 52 km/h
(to nearest km/h)

b) 22 skiers **c)** 20 skiers

Q2 **a)**

Weight (kg)	Tally	Frequency	Mid-Interval	Frequency × Mid-Interval
200 ≤ w < 250	IIII	4	225	900
250 ≤ w < 300	IIII	5	275	1375
300 ≤ w < 350	IIII II	7	325	2275
350 ≤ w < 400	II	2	375	750

b) 294 kg (to nearest kg)
c) 300 ≤ w < 350 kg

Q3 **a)**

Number	0≤n<0.2	0.2≤n<0.4	0.4≤n<0.6	0.6≤n<0.8	0.8≤n<1
Tally	IIII IIII II	IIII I	IIII IIII II	IIII IIII	IIII III
Frequency	12	6	12	10	8
Mid-Interval	0.1	0.3	0.5	0.7	0.9
Frequency × Mid-Interval	1.2	1.8	6	7	7.2

b) 0 ≤ n < 0.2 and 0.4 ≤ n < 0.6
c) 0.4 ≤ n < 0.6
d) 0.483 (3 d.p.)

Cumulative Frequency P.25-P.26

Q1 accept:
a) 133-134 **c)** 136-137
b) 127-128 **d)** 8-10

Q2 **a)** 90 years
b) 120 years
c) 70 years

Q3 **a)**

No. passengers	0≤n<50	50≤n<100	100≤n<150	150≤n<200	200≤n<250	250≤n<300
Frequency	2	7	10	5	3	1
Cumulative Frequency	2	9	19	24	27	28
Mid-Interval	25	75	125	175	225	275
Frequency × Mid-Interval	50	525	1250	875	675	275

Estimated mean = 130 passengers
(to nearest whole number)

b)

accept median of 118-122 passengers
c) 100 ≤ n < 150

Q4 **a)**

Mark (%)	0 ≤ m < 20	20 ≤ m < 40	40 ≤ m < 60	60 ≤ m < 80	80 ≤ m < 100
Frequency	2	12	18	5	3
Cumulative Frequency	2	14	32	37	40

b) 36%-38%
c) 19%-21%
d) 45%-47%

Q5

Score	31≤s<41	41≤s<51	51≤s<61	61≤s<71	71≤s<81	81≤s<91	91≤s<101
Frequency	4	12	21	32	19	8	4
Cumulative Frequency	4	16	37	69	88	96	100

a) 61 ≤ s < 71
b) 61 ≤ s < 71
c)

median = 65 (accept 64-66)
d) 73 – 55 = 18 (accept 17-19)

Q6 **a)**

Life (hours)	Frequency	Cumulative Frequency
900 ≤ L < 1000	10	10
1000 ≤ L < 1100	12	22
1100 ≤ L < 1200	15	37
1200 ≤ L < 1300	18	55
1300 ≤ L < 1400	22	77
1400 ≤ L < 1500	17	94
1500 ≤ L < 1600	14	108
1600 ≤ L < 1700	9	117

b) 1300 ≤ L < 1400

Answers: P.27 — P.30

c)

median = 1320 hours (±20)

d) lower quartile = 1150 (±20)
upper quartile = 1460 (±20)

Q7 a)

Time	2:00 ≤ t < 2:30	2:30 ≤ t < 3:00	3:00 ≤ t < 3:30	3:30 ≤ t < 4:00	4:00 ≤ t < 4:30
Tally	1	ʻʰʰʰ	ʰʰʰ ʰʰʰ ʰʰʰ	ʰʰʰ 11	111
Frequency	1	5	14	7	3
Cumulative Frequency	1	6	20	27	30

b)

c) median = 3:19 (±3)
upper quartile = 3:37 (±3)
lower quartile = 3:05 (±3)

d) 0:32 (±5)

Histograms and Dispersion
P.27-P.29

Q1 4 × 10 = 40 people

Q2 a)

Weight (kg)	0≤w<2	2≤w<4	4≤w<7	7≤w<9	9≤w<15
Frequency	3	2	6	9	12
Frequency density	1.5	1	2	4.5	2

b)

c) 23 hives

Q3 (A,I), (B,II)

Q4 a)

No. of hours	Frequency	Frequency density
0 ≤ h < 1	6	6
1 ≤ h < 3	13	6.5
3 ≤ h < 5	15	7.5
5 ≤ h < 8	9	3
8 ≤ h < 10	23	11.5
10 ≤ h < 15	25	5
15 ≤ h < 20	12	2.4

b) 103 students

---

c)

d) 41 students

Q5 A — 16 year olds

B — bags of sugar

Q6 a)

Salary (£1000s)	0 ≤ x < 10	10 ≤ x < 20	20 ≤ x < 30	30 ≤ x < 40	40 ≤ x < 50
Frequency	10	25	42	20	3
Frequency Density	1	2.5	4.2	2	0.3

b) E.g. there are more people with higher salaries now than 10 years ago.

Q7 a)

Amount of Milk (Litres)	Frequency	Frequency Density	Mid-Interval	Frequency × Mid-Interval
0 < C < 1	6	6	0.5	3
1 < C < 5	6	1.5	3	18
5 < C < 8	6	2	6.5	39
8 < C < 10	6	3	9	54
10 < C < 15	6	1.2	12.5	75
15 < C < 20	6	1.2	17.5	105

b) 8.2 litres (to 1 d.p.)

c)

d) 18 days

Q8 a)

Amount (£)	Frequency	Frequency Density	Mid-Interval	Frequency × Mid-Interval
0 ≤ A < 0.50	11	22	0.25	2.75
0.50 ≤ A < 1.00	25	50	0.75	18.75
1.00 ≤ A < 1.30	9	30	1.15	10.35
1.30 ≤ A < 1.50	12	60	1.40	16.80
1.50 ≤ A < 1.80	24	80	1.65	39.60
1.80 ≤ A < 2.50	21	30	2.15	45.15
2.50 ≤ A < 3.10	54	90	2.80	151.20
3.10 ≤ A < 4.10	32	32	3.60	115.20

mean = £2.13 (to nearest penny)

b) 2.50 ≤ A < 3.10

---

c)

(0.5 × 22) + (0.5 × 50)
+ (0.3 × 30) + (0.1 × 60)
= 51 readers

d) No. 51 readers receive less than £1.40.
So 188 − 51 = 137 receive £1.40 or more.
But 75% of 188 = 141.

Scatter Graphs P.30-P.31

Q1 (A,S), (B,R), (C,P), (D,U)

Q2 a)

b) There is no correlation.

c) No — if he were correct the graph would show negative correlation.

Q3 a)

b) Strong positive correlation.

c) Yes

Q4 a)

Positively correlated.

c) E.g. The taller the person, the bigger their shoe size.

d) 9

Q5 **a), b)**

c) Candidate 5.

d) 50%

Q6 **a), b)**

c) £7.50 (±20p)

Q7 **a)**

b) i) 20 (to nearest whole number)

ii) £140 (± £10)

c) The data is negatively correlated.

Stem and Leaf Diagrams P.32

Q1 3, 3, 3, 5, 8, 8, 9, 12, 13, 14, 14, 18, 18, 19, 20, 22, 22, 24, 31, 33.

Q2 **a)** 2   **b)** 4

    c) 6   **d)** 39

    e) 34   **f)** 21

    g) 21.24   **h)** 21

Q3

```
0 | 7 8
1 | 1 3 5 8
2 | 1 2 3 6 9
3 | 1 3 7 9
4 | 1 8
5 | 0
```

Q4

```
40 | 1 2
35 | 0 0 1 1 1 2 3 3 4
30 | 0 0 0 0 0 0 0 0 0 0 0 1 1 1 1 1 1 1 1 2 2 2 2 2 2 3 3 3 3 4 4 4 4
25 | 0 0 0 0 0 1 1 1 1 1 1 2 2 2 2 2 3 3 3 3 3 3 3 3 4 4 4 4 4 4 4 4 4 4 4
20 | 1 3 3 4 4 4 4
```

E.g. | Key: 20|1 means 21 |

Pie Charts P.33

Q1 $\frac{360°}{100} = 3.6°$ per gram

Carbohydrate 3.6 × 35 = 126°

Protein   3.6 × 15 = 54°

Fat   3.6 × 10 = 36°

Magical Fairy Dust   3.6 × 40 = 144°

Q2 Sherrington 380,000 = 148° (approx) 2600 visitors = 1°

So, to the nearest 10,000:

Brompton = 2600 × 118° ≈ 310,000

Barny = 2600 × 44° ≈ 110,000

Livsea = 2600 × 50° ≈ 130,000

Q3 Part **c)**

Q4 It's not possible to tell whether more people voted for the Green Party in 2009, because you can't tell how many people voted in either election.

Graphs and Charts P.34

Q1 **a)**

b) 22

c) 19

Q2 **a)** Tally chart

Level of skier	No.
Beginner	卌 lll
Intermediate	卌 卌
Good	llll
Very good	lll
Racer	lll

b) Bar chart

c) Most common type of skier is Intermediate.

Q3 Complaints have not "tailed off" - they have remained the same (approx 10,850) per month.

The number of complaints is not increasing but there are still 10,850 per month, every month.

The products cannot possibly be getting made to a higher quality if the complaints remain the same each month.

Probability P.35-P.38

Q1 **a)** 1/2

    b) 2/3

    c) 1/6

    d) 0

And so should be arranged approximately like this on the number line.

Q2 Debbie's chance of winning would be 1/9. This is greater than 0.1, so she would choose to play.

Q3 The probability of a head is still 1/2

Q4 1 − 0.27 = 0.73 or 73/100

Q5 **a)** 5/12

    b) 4/12 = 1/3

    c) 3/12 = 1/4

    d) 9/12 = 3/4

Q6 **a)** 40/132 = 10/33

    b) P(car being blue or green) = 45/132

    P(not blue or green) = 87/132

    = 29/44

Q7 **a)** 1/4

    b) 1/4 × 100 = approx 25 days

Q8 **a)**

Outcome	Frequency
W	8
D	5
L	7

b) The 3 outcomes are not equally likely.

c) 1/4

d) They are most likely to win.

Q9 **a)** $\frac{1}{13}$

    b) $\frac{2}{39}$ **c)** $\frac{1}{36}$

Q10 **a)** $\frac{7}{12}$ **b)** $\frac{7}{12}$

    c) The two are not mutually exclusive (or other equivalent answer).

Q11 **a)** $\frac{2}{5}$

    b) $\frac{4}{15}$ **c)** $\frac{2}{3}$

Q12 **a)** (1,1), (1,2), (1,3), (1,4), (1,5), (1,6), (1,7), (2,1), (2,2), (2,3), (2,4), (2,5), (2,6), (2,7), (3,1), (3,2), (3,3), (3,4), (3,5), (3,6), (3,7)

Answers: P.37 — P.43

b)

	1	2	3	4	5	6	7
1	2	3	4	5	6	7	8
2	3	4	5	6	7	8	9
3	4	5	6	7	8	9	10

c) $\frac{1}{7}$ **d)** $\frac{11}{21}$

e) $\frac{2}{7}$ **f)** $\frac{5}{7}$

g) Subtract answer to part **e)** from 1.

Q13 a)

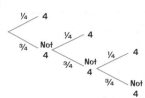

b) $\frac{18}{35}$

c) $\frac{3}{7}$

Q14 4 times

Q15

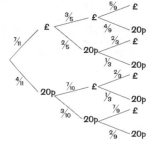

a) $\frac{3}{16}$

b) $\frac{37}{64}$

Q16 a)

b) $\frac{28}{55}$ **c)** $\frac{46}{165}$

Q17 a) $\frac{1}{4}$ **b)** $\frac{1}{2}$

c) $\frac{1}{2}$

Q18 $\frac{1}{28}$

Unit 2 — Number and Algebra

Types of Number P.39

Q1 4

Q2 -3 °C

Q3 the third cube number (27)

Q4 a) 17, 19, 23, 29
b) 81, 121, 169, 225

Q5 a) 2   **b)** e.g. 29
c) 19   **d)** 19 and 2
e) e.g. 1 or 25

Q6 a)

1	②	③	4	⑤	6	⑦	8	9	10
⑪	12	⑬	14	15	16	⑰	18	⑲	20
21	22	㉓	24	25	26	27	28	㉙	30
㉛	32	33	34	35	36	�37	38	39	40
㊶	42	㊸	44	45	46	㊼	48	49	50
51	52	㊾53	54	55	56	57	58	㊾59	60
㊿61	62	63	64	65	66	㊿67	68	69	70
㉛71	72	⑦73	74	75	76	77	78	⑦79	80
81	82	⑧83	84	85	86	87	88	⑧89	90
91	92	93	94	95	96	⑨97	98	99	100

b) 3 of: 11 (11), 13 (31), 17 (71), 37 (73), 79 (97)
c) e.g. 3 is a factor of 27

Q7 113

Q8 There's just one: 2 is the only even prime.

Powers P.40-P.41

Q1 a) 16
b) 1000
c) $3 \times 3 \times 3 \times 3 \times 3 = 243$
d) $4 \times 4 \times 4 \times 4 \times 4 \times 4 = 4096$
e) $1 \times 1 \times 1 \times 1 \times 1 \times 1 \times 1 \times 1 \times 1 = 1$
f) $5 \times 5 \times 5 \times 5 \times 5 \times 5 = 15\,625$

Q2 a) 2^8 (or 256)   **b)** 12^5 (or 248 832)
c) x^5 **d)** m^3
e) y^4 **f)** z^6

Q3 b) 10^7
c) 10^6
d) 10^8
e) Simply add the powers.

Q4 b) 2^3
c) 4^2
d) 8^3
e) Simply subtract the powers.

Q5 a) true   **b)** true
c) false   **d)** false
e) true   **f)** false
g) false   **h)** true
i) false   **j)** true
k) true   **l)** false

Q6 a) 3^{-3} **d)** 3^{-12}
b) 4^{25} **e)** 4^6
c) 10^{-13} **f)** 5^3

Q7 a) 10^2 **b)** 8^4
c) 6^5 **d)** x^5
e) a^9 **f)** p^{15}

Q8 a) False, correct answer is 1/8
b) False, correct answer is 1
c) True
d) True
e) False, $3^2 = 9$
f) True

Q9 a) 6^4 **e)** 4^{-1}
b) 6^6 **f)** 3^{-1}
c) $2^1 = 2$ **g)** 5^3
d) 3^2 **h)** 2^{15}

Q10 a) 1   **g)** 0.5
b) 35   **h)** 0.2
c) $\frac{1}{2} = 0.5$ **i)** 5
d) $\frac{1}{1000} = 0.001$ **j)** 27
e) 100   **k)** 8
f) 16

Q11 a) $\frac{4}{9}$ **d)** $\frac{5}{2} = 2\,½$
b) $\frac{27}{125}$ **e)** $\frac{1}{25}$
c) $\frac{9}{4} = 2\,¼$

Manipulating Surds and Use of π P.42-P.43

Q1 e.g. 3, $3\frac{1}{2}$, 4 are all rational and
$\sqrt{6}\,\sqrt{7}$, $\sqrt{8}$, are all irrational.

Q2 a) e.g. $x = 2$
b) e.g. $x = 4$

Q3 a) irrational
b) rational
c) irrational
d) rational

Q4 a) $\sqrt{2} \times \sqrt{8}$, $(\sqrt{5})^6$, 0.4,
$40 - 2^{-1} - 4^{-2}$, $49^{-\frac{1}{2}}$
b) $\frac{\sqrt{3}}{\sqrt{2}}$, $(\sqrt{7})^3$, 6π, $\sqrt{5} - 2.1$, $\sqrt{6} + 6$

Q5 a) rational
b) irrational
c) rational

Q6 e.g. $x = \sqrt{18}$, $y = \sqrt{2}$ gives
$\frac{x}{y} = \sqrt{9} = 3$.

Q7 a) e.g. 1.5   **b)** e.g. $\sqrt{2}$
c) As P is rational, let $P = \frac{a}{b}$ where a and b
are integers. $\frac{1}{P} = \frac{b}{a}$ which is rational.

Q8 a) $xyz = 4\sqrt{6}$, irrational
b) $(xyz)^2 = 96$, rational
c) $x + yz = 2 + 2\sqrt{6}$, irrational
d) $\frac{yz}{2\sqrt{3x}} = \frac{2\sqrt{6}}{2\sqrt{6}} = 1$, rational

Q9 3π cm^2

Q10 a) $\sqrt{15}$ **e)** x
b) 2   **f)** x
c) 1   **g)** 8
d) $2½$ **h)** $3[\sqrt{2} - 1]$

Q11 a) $(1 + \sqrt{5})(1 - \sqrt{5}) = -4$, rational
b) $\frac{1 + \sqrt{5}}{1 - \sqrt{5}} = -\frac{1}{2}(3 + \sqrt{5})$, irrational

Q12 a) $(x + y)(x - y) = -1$, rational
b) $\frac{x + y}{x - y} = -3 - 2\sqrt{2}$, irrational

Q13 a) $\frac{\sqrt{2}}{2}$ **e)** $\sqrt{2} - 1$
b) $\frac{\sqrt{2}}{2}$ **f)** $3 - \sqrt{3}$
c) $\frac{\sqrt{10}a}{10}$ **g)** $\frac{2[\sqrt{6} - 1]}{5}$
d) $\frac{\sqrt{xy}}{y}$ **h)** $\frac{3 + \sqrt{5}}{2}$

Multiples, Factors and Primes P.44-P.45

Q1 a) 12   **b)** 3
c) 1, 9   **d)** 1, 3, 9
e) P = 12, Q = 6

UNIT 2 — NUMBER AND ALGEBRA

Answers: P.44 — P.52

Q2 Any 5 of:
2 groups of 24, 3 groups of 16,
4 groups of 12, 6 groups of 8,
8 groups of 6, 12 groups of 4,
16 groups of 3, 24 groups of 2.

Q3 The Conversational French and Woodturning classes both have a prime number of pupils and so cannot be divided into equal groups.

Q4
a) 1, 8, 27, 64, 125
b) 8, 64
c) 27
d) 8, 64
e) 125

Q5
a) 2×3^2　　b) $2^2 \times 5 \times 7$
c) 47

Q6
a) 2, 3, 5, 7, 11　b) 28
c) $2^2 \times 7$

Q7
a) 1, 3, 5, 7, 9
b) 25
c) 5^2

Q8
a) 495　　　b) $3 \times 5 \times 11$

Q9
a) 1, 4, 9, 16, 25, 36, 49, 64, 81, 100
b) 4, 16, 36, 64, 100
c) 9, 36, 81
d) 1, 64
e) Total = 55 = 5×11

Q10
a) $50 \times 25 \times 16 = 20{,}000 \text{ cm}^3$
b) $2^5 \times 5^4$
c) 200. It is not enough to divide the large volume by the smaller volume as the shapes of the blocks are important too. It is possible to fit $16 \div 4 = 4$ small blocks across the width, $50 \div 5 = 10$ small blocks along the length and $25 \div 5 = 5$ small blocks down the height of the large block. This enables Gordon to fit $4 \times 10 \times 5 = 200$ small blocks into the big block

Q11
a) 680　　　b) $2^2 \times 5 \times 17$
c) $2 \times 5 \times 17$　　d) 5×17

Q12 42

LCM and HCF P.46

Q1
a) 6, 12, 18, 24, 30, 36, 42, 48, 54, 60
b) 5, 10, 15, 20, 25, 30, 35, 40, 45, 50
c) 30

Q2
a) 1, 2, 3, 5, 6, 10, 15, 30
b) 1, 2, 3, 4, 6, 8, 12, 16, 24, 48
c) 6

Q3
a) 20　　　b) 10
c) 2　　　d) 15
e) 15　　　f) 5
g) 32　　　h) 16
i) 16

Q4
a) 120　　　b) 120
c) 120　　　d) 45
e) 90　　　f) 180
g) 64　　　h) 192
i) 192

Q5
a) 7th June
b) 16th June
c) Sunday (1st July)
d) Lars

Fractions, Decimals and Percentages P.47-P.48

Q1
a) 25%　　　b) 50%
c) 75%　　　d) 10%
e) 41.52%　　f) 84.06%
g) 39.62%　　h) 28.28%

Q2
a) 0.5　　　b) 0.12
c) 0.4　　　d) 0.34
e) 0.602　　f) 0.549
g) 0.431　　h) 0.788

Q3
a) 50%　　　b) 25%
c) 12.5%　　d) 75%
e) 4%　　　f) 66.7%
g) 26.7%　　h) 28.6%

Q4
a) 1/4　　　b) 3/5
c) 9/20　　　d) 3/10
e) 41/500　　f) 62/125
g) 443/500　　h) 81/250

Q5 85%

Q6 Grade C

Q7
a) 0.3　　　e) 1.75
b) 0.37　　　f) 0.125
c) 0.4　　　g) 0.6
d) 0.375　　h) 0.05

Q8

Fraction	Decimal
½	0.5
⅕	0.2
⅛	0.125
8⁄5	1.6
4⁄16	0.25
7⁄2	3.5
x⁄10	0.x
x⁄100	0.0x
3⁄20	0.15
9⁄20	0.45

Q9
a) $0.\dot{5}$　　　e) $0.\overline{90}$
b) $0.\dot{7}$　　　f) $0.\overline{29}$
c) $0.\overline{63}$　　g) $0.\overline{478}$
d) $0.\overline{47}$　　h) $0.\overline{589}$

Q10
a) $\frac{3}{5}$　　　e) $\frac{1}{3}$
b) $\frac{3}{4}$　　　f) $\frac{2}{3}$
c) $\frac{19}{20}$　　g) $\frac{1}{9}$
d) $\frac{16}{125}$

Q11
a) $\frac{2}{9}$　　　e) $\frac{4}{33}$
b) $\frac{4}{9}$　　　f) $\frac{545}{999}$
c) $\frac{8}{9}$　　　g) $\frac{251}{333}$
d) $\frac{80}{99}$　　h) $\frac{52}{333}$

Fractions P.49-P.50

Q1
a) $\frac{1}{64}$　　　b) $\frac{1}{9}$
c) $\frac{1}{18}$　　　d) $3\frac{29}{32}$
e) $5\frac{5}{32}$　　　f) $\frac{81}{100\,000}$

Q2
a) 1　　　b) 4
c) $\frac{1}{2}$　　　d) $\frac{2}{5}$

e) $\frac{10}{33}$　　　f) 1000

Q3
a) $\frac{1}{4}$　　　b) $\frac{5}{6}$
c) $\frac{1}{2}$　　　d) $4\frac{3}{8}$
e) $5\frac{3}{8}$　　　f) 1

Q4 $3\frac{7}{15}$, so the bowl will be big enough.

Q5
a) 0　　　b) $\frac{1}{2}$
c) $-\frac{1}{6}$　　　d) $1\frac{7}{8}$
e) $-3\frac{1}{8}$　　　f) $\frac{4}{5}$

Q6
a) $\frac{3}{4}$　　　b) $\frac{5}{12}$
c) $\frac{7}{15}$　　　d) $4\frac{3}{4}$
e) 4　　　f) $1\frac{1}{5}$
g) $\frac{5}{8}$　　　h) $-\frac{1}{24}$
i) $4\frac{3}{5}$　　　j) $1\frac{1}{30}$
k) 1　　　l) $\frac{44}{75}$

Q7
a) 1/12　　　b) 1/4
c) 2/3

Q8
a) 3/4 of the programme
b) 5/8 of the programme
c) 1/8 of the programme

Q9 3/5 of the kitchen staff are girls.
2/5 of the employees are boys

Q10 7/30 of those asked had no opinion.

Q11
a) 12/30 = 2/5
b) 6 days

Q12
a) Each box will hold 16 sandwiches. So 5 boxes will be needed for 80 sandwiches.
b) 25 inches tall

Ratios P.51

Q1
a) £8, £12
b) 80 m, 70 m
c) 100 g, 200 g, 200 g.
d) 3 hrs, 6 hrs, 9 hrs.

Q2
a) £4.80　　　b) 80 cm

Q3 John 4, Peter 12

Q4 400 ml, 600 ml, 1000 ml

Q5 Jane £40, Holly £48, Rosemary £12

Q6 Paul — £16

Q7
a) £39　　　b) £140

Q8
a) 15 kg　　　b) 30 kg
c) 8 kg cement, 24 kg sand and 48 kg gravel.

Basic Algebra P.52-P.54

Q1
a) -27°C　　　d) +18°C
b) -22°C　　　e) +15°C
c) +12°C　　　f) -12°C

Q2 Expression b) is larger by 1.

Q3
a) $-4x$　　　b) $18y$

Q4
a) −1000, −10　　c) 144, 16
b) −96, −6　　　d) 0, 0

Answers: P.53 — P.58

Q5   -4

Q6   **a)** $-6xy$ **g)** $\dfrac{-5x}{y}$

b) $-16ab$ **h)** 3

c) $8x^2$ **i)** -4

d) $-16p^2$ **j)** -10

e) $\dfrac{10x}{y}$ **k)** $4x$

f) $\dfrac{-10x}{y}$ **l)** $-8y$

Q7   **a)** $15x^2 - x$

b) $13x^2 - 5x$

c) $-7x^2 + 12x + 12$

d) $30abc + 12ab + 4b$

e) $18pq + 8p$

f) $17ab - 17a + b$

g) $4pq - 5p - 9q$

h) $16x^2 - 4y^2$

i) $abc + 10ab - 11cd$

j) $-2x^2 + y^2 - z^2 + 6xy$

Q8   **a)** $4x + 4y - 4z$

b) $x^2 + 5x$

c) $-3x + 6$

d) $9a + 9b$

e) $-a + 4b$

f) $2x - 6$

g) $4e^2 - 2f^2 + 10ef$

h) $16m - 8n$

i) $6x^2 + 2x$

j) $-2ab + 11$

k) $-2x^2 - xz - 2yz$

l) $3x - 6y - 5$

m) $-3a - 4b$

n) $14pqr + 8pq + 35qr$

o) $x^3 + x^2$

p) $4x^3 + 8x^2 + 4x$

q) $8a^2b + 24ab + 8ab^2$

r) $7p^2q + 7pq^2 - 7q$

s) $16x - 8y$

Q9   **a)** $x^2 + 4x + 3x + 12 = x^2 + 7x + 12$

b) $4x^2 + 6x + 6x + 9 = 4x^2 + 12x + 9$

c) $15x^2 + 3x + 10x + 2 = 15x^2 + 13x + 2$

Q10 **a)** $x^2 - 2x - 3$

b) $x^2 + 2x - 15$

c) $x^2 + 13x + 30$

d) $x^2 - 7x + 10$

e) $x^2 - 5x - 14$

f) $28 - 11x + x^2$

g) $6x - 2 + 9x^2 - 3x = 9x^2 + 3x - 2$

h) $6x^2 - 12x + 4x - 8 = 6x^2 - 8x - 8$

i) $4x^2 + x - 12x - 3 = 4x^2 - 11x - 3$

j) $4x^2 - 8xy + 2xy - 4y^2$
$= 4x^2 - 4y^2 - 6xy$

k) $12x^2 - 8xy + 24xy - 16y^2$
$= 12x^2 - 16y^2 + 16xy$

l) $9x^2 + 4y^2 + 12xy$

Q11 $15x^2 + 10x - 6x - 4 = 15x^2 + 4x - 4$

Q12 $4x^2 - 4x + 1$

Q13 **a)** $(4x + 6)$ m

b) $(-3x^2 + 17x - 10)$ m²

Q14 **a)** $(8x + 20)$ cm

b) $40x$ cm²

c) $40x - 12x = 28x$ cm²

Q15 **a)** Perimeter — $3x + 29$ cm

Area — $\dfrac{7x + 126}{2}$ cm²

b) Perimeter — $(8x + 4)$ cm
Area — $(3x^2 + 14x - 24)$ cm²

c) Perimeter — $(16x - 4)$ cm
Area — $(16x^2 - 8x + 1)$ cm²

d) Perimeter — $(10x + 4)$ cm
Area — $(6x^2 - 5x - 6)$ cm²

Q16 **a)** $(x + 3)(x - 3)$

b) $(y + 4)(y - 4)$

c) $(5 + z)(5 - z)$

d) $(6 + a)(6 - a)$

e) $(2x + 3)(2x - 3)$

f) $(3y + 2)(3y - 2)$

g) $(5 + 4z)(5 - 4z)$

h) $(1 + 6a)(1 - 6a)$

i) $(x^2 + 6)(x^2 - 6)$

j) $(x^2 + y^2)(x^2 - y^2)$

k) $(1 + ab)(1 - ab)$

l) $(10x + 12y)(10x - 12y)$

Q17 **a)** $(x + 2)(x - 2)$

b) $(12 + y^2)(12 - y^2)$

c) $(1 + 3xy)(1 - 3xy)$

d) $(7x^2y^2 + 1)(7x^2y^2 - 1)$

Q18 **a)** $a^2(b + c)$

b) $a^2(5 + 13b)$

c) $a^2(2b + 3c)$

d) $a^2(a + y)$

e) $a^2(2x + 3y + 4z)$

f) $a^2(b^2 + ac^2)$

Q19 **a)** $4xyz(1 + 2) = 12xyz$

b) $4xyz(2 + 3) = 20xyz$

c) $8xyz(1 + 2x)$

d) $4xyz^2(5xy + 4)$

Algebraic Fractions P.55-P.56

Q1   **a)** $\dfrac{3xy}{z}$ **c)** $\dfrac{1}{3xy^2z^3}$

b) $\dfrac{12b^2}{c}$ **d)** $\dfrac{q^3}{2r^3}$

Q2   **a)** $\dfrac{2}{xy}$ **g)** $\dfrac{x^3}{5}$

b) $\dfrac{3a^2b}{2}$ **h)** $\dfrac{12a^3b^2}{5}$

c) $\dfrac{y}{2x^2}$ **i)** $\dfrac{3a^4c^3}{2bd}$

d) $\dfrac{2qr^2}{3}$ **j)** 1

e) $\dfrac{8x^2z^2}{y}$ **k)** $\dfrac{3rt^2}{2}$

f) $\dfrac{90ac^4}{b}$ **l)** $\dfrac{d^6}{e^3f}$

Q3   **a)** $2x^2y$ **g)** $\dfrac{12yz}{x}$

b) a **h)** $\dfrac{4a^3}{b}$

c) $\dfrac{3x^2}{y}$ **i)** $\dfrac{5a^3}{b}$

d) $\dfrac{pq}{2}$ **j)** $\dfrac{2x}{y^2z}$

e) $2ef$ **k)** $\dfrac{6}{n}$

f) $5x^3$ **l)** $\dfrac{7g}{f}$

Q4   **a)** $x = 5$ **b)** $x = 2$

Q5   **a)** $\dfrac{3 + y}{2x}$ **g)** $\dfrac{3x + 2 + y}{24}$

b) $\dfrac{1 + y}{x}$ **h)** $\dfrac{x + 2y - 2}{10}$

c) $\dfrac{2xy}{z}$ **i)** $\dfrac{7x}{6}$

d) $\dfrac{6x + 1}{3}$ **j)** $\dfrac{37x}{42}$

e) $\dfrac{7x + 6}{x}$ **k)** $\dfrac{x(y + 3)}{3y}$

f) $\dfrac{14x + y}{6}$ **l)** $\dfrac{xyz + 4x + 4z}{4y}$

Q6   **a)** $\dfrac{4x - 5y}{3}$ **g)** $\dfrac{z}{15}$

b) $\dfrac{4x - 1}{y}$ **h)** $\dfrac{m(12 - n)}{3n}$

c) $\dfrac{4x + 3y - 2}{2x}$ **i)** $\dfrac{b(14 - a)}{7a}$

d) $\dfrac{2 - 2x}{x}$ **j)** $\dfrac{-p + 5q}{10}$

e) $\dfrac{-1}{4x}$ **k)** $\dfrac{-3p - 4q}{4}$

f) $\dfrac{4x - y}{6}$ **l)** $\dfrac{9x - 4y + xy}{3y}$

Q7   **a)** $\dfrac{a^2}{b^2}$ **f)** $\dfrac{11}{6x}$

b) 1 **g)** $\dfrac{2(a^2 + b^2)}{a^2 - b^2}$

c) $\dfrac{3}{2r}$ **h)** $\dfrac{3}{4}$

d) $\dfrac{mn(pm + 1)}{p^2}$ **i)** $\dfrac{3x - 6y}{8}$

e) $\dfrac{2x}{x^2 - y^2}$

Solving Equations P.57-P.58

Q1   1

Q2   **a)** $x = \pm 3$ **d)** $x = \pm 3$

b) $x = \pm 6$ **e)** $x = \pm 1$

c) $x = \pm 3$

Q3   **a)** $x = 5$ **d)** $x = -6$

b) $x = 4$ **e)** $x = 5$

c) $x = 10$ **f)** $x = 9$

Q4   **a)** $x = 5$ **e)** $x = 6$

b) $x = 2$ **f)** $x = 5$

c) $x = 8$ **g)** $x = \pm 2$

d) $x = 17$

Q5   **a)** 15.5 cm **b)** 37.2 cm

Q6   £15.50

Q7   **a)** $x = 9$ **g)** $x = 15$

b) $x = 2$ **h)** $x = 110$

c) $x = 3$ **i)** $x = \pm 6$

d) $x = 3$ **j)** $x = 66$

e) $x = 4$ **k)** $x = 700$

f) $x = -1$ **l)** $x = 7\frac{1}{2}$

Q8   **a)** Joan — £x
Kate — £$2x$
Linda — £$(x - 232)$

b) $x + 2x + (x - 232) = 2400$
$4x - 232 = 2400$
$4x = 2632$
$x = 658$

c) Kate — £1316
Linda — £426

Q9   **a)** $2x + 32$ cm

b) $12x$ cm²

c) $x = 3.2$

Q10 **a)** $x = 0.75$ **d)** $x = -1$

b) $x = -1$ **e)** $x = 4$

c) $x = -6$ **f)** $x = 13$

Q11 $x = 8$

Q12 $x = 1$

Q13 8 yrs

Q14 39, 35, 8

Q15 **a)** $y = 22$ **f)** $x = 7$

b) $x = 8$ **g)** $x = \pm 3$

c) $z = -5$ **h)** $x = \pm 4$

Answers: P.59 — P.62

d) $x = 19$ **i)** $x = \pm 7$
e) $x = 23$

Q16 $x = 1\frac{1}{2}$

Q17 a) $x = 5$ **b)** $x = 9$

Q18 $x = 1\frac{1}{2}$ $AB = 5$ cm
$AC = 5\frac{1}{2}$ cm
$BC = 7\frac{1}{2}$ cm

Rearranging Formulas P.59-P.60

Q1 a) $h = \dfrac{10 - g}{4}$

b) $c = 2d - 4$

c) $k = 3 + \dfrac{j}{2}$

d) $b = \dfrac{3a}{2}$

e) $g = \dfrac{8f}{3}$

f) $x = 2(y + 3)$

g) $t = 6(s - 10)$

h) $q = \dfrac{\sqrt{p}}{2}$

Q2 a) $c = \dfrac{w - 500m}{50}$

b) 132

Q3 a) i) £38.00   **ii)** £48.00
b) $c = 28 + 0.25n$
c) $n = 4(c - 28)$
d) i) 24 miles **ii)** 88 miles
iii) 114 miles

Q4 a) $x = \sqrt{y + 2}$

b) $x = y^2 - 3$

c) $s = 2\sqrt{r}$

d) $g = 3f - 10$

e) $z = 5 - 2w$

f) $x = \sqrt{\dfrac{3v}{h}}$

g) $a = \dfrac{v^2 - u^2}{2s}$

h) $u = \sqrt{v^2 - 2as}$

i) $g = \dfrac{4\pi^2 l}{t^2}$

Q5 a) £Jx

b) $P = T - Jx$

c) $J = \dfrac{T - P}{x}$

d) £16

Q6 a) i) £2.04   **ii)** £3.48
b) $C = (12x + 60)$ pence
c) $x = \dfrac{C - 60}{12}$
d) i) 36   **ii)** 48   **iii)** 96

Q7 a) $x = \dfrac{z}{y + 2}$

b) $x = \dfrac{b}{a - 3}$

c) $x = \dfrac{y}{4 - z}$

d) $x = \dfrac{3z + y}{y + 5}$

e) $x = \dfrac{-2}{y - z}$ or $\dfrac{2}{z - y}$

f) $x = \dfrac{2y + 3z}{2 - z}$

g) $x = \dfrac{-y - wz}{yz - 1}$ or $\dfrac{y + wz}{1 - yz}$

h) $x = \dfrac{-z}{4}$

Q8 a) $p = \dfrac{4r - 2q}{q - 3}$

b) $g = \dfrac{5 - 2e}{f + 2}$

c) $b = \dfrac{3c + 2a}{a - c}$

d) $q = \pm\sqrt{\dfrac{4}{p - r}} = \pm\dfrac{2}{\sqrt{p - r}}$

e) $a = \dfrac{2c + 4b}{4 + c - d}$

f) $x = \pm\sqrt{\dfrac{-3y}{2}}$

g) $k = \pm\sqrt{\dfrac{14}{h - 1}}$

h) $x = \left(\dfrac{4 - y}{2 - z}\right)^2$

i) $a = \dfrac{b^2}{3 + b}$

j) $m = -7n$

k) $e = \dfrac{d}{50}$

l) $y = \dfrac{x}{3x + 2}$

Q9 a) $y = \dfrac{x}{x - 1}$

b) $y = \dfrac{-3 - 2x}{x - 1}$ or $\dfrac{2x + 3}{1 - x}$

c) $y = \pm\sqrt{\dfrac{x + 1}{2x - 1}}$

d) $y = \pm\sqrt{\dfrac{1 + 2x}{3x - 2}}$

Factorising Quadratics P.61

Q1 a) $(x + 5)(x - 2)$
$x = -5, x = 2$
b) $(x - 3)(x - 2)$
$x = 3, x = 2$
c) $(x - 1)^2$
$x = 1$
d) $(x - 3)(x - 1)$
$x = 3, x = 1$
e) $(x - 5)(x + 4)$
$x = 5, x = -4$
f) $(x + 1)(x - 5)$
$x = -1, x = 5$
g) $(x + 7)(x - 1)$
$x = -7, x = 1$
h) $(x + 7)^2$
$x = -7$
i) $(x - 5)(x + 3)$
$x = 5, x = -3$

Q2 a) $(x + 8)(x - 2)$
$x = -8, x = 2$
b) $(x + 9)(x - 4)$
$x = -9, x = 4$
c) $(x + 9)(x - 5)$
$x = -9, x = 5$
d) $x(x - 5)$
$x = 0, x = 5$
e) $x(x - 11)$
$x = 0, x = 11$
f) $(x - 7)(x + 3)$
$x = 7, x = -3$
g) $(x - 30)(x + 10)$
$x = 30, x = -10$

h) $(x - 24)(x - 2)$
$x = 24, x = 2$
i) $(x - 9)(x - 4)$
$x = 9, x = 4$
j) $(x + 7)(x - 2)$
$x = -7, x = 2$
k) $(x + 7)(x - 3)$
$x = -7, x = 3$
l) $(x - 5)(x + 2)$
$x = 5, x = -2$
m) $(x - 6)(x + 3)$
$x = 6, x = -3$
n) $(x - 9)(x + 7)$
$x = 9, x = -7$
o) $(x + 4)(x - 3)$
$x = -4, x = 3$

Q3 $x = \frac{1}{2}, x = -\frac{1}{2}$

Q4 $x = 4$

Q5 a) $(x^2 - x)$ m^2 **b)** $x = 3$

Q6 a) $x(x + 1)$ cm^2 **b)** $x = 3$

Q7 a) x^2 m^2 **b)** $12x$ m^2
c) $x^2 + 12x - 64 = 0$
$x = 4$

Completing the Square P.62

Q1 a) $(x - 2)^2 - 9$
b) $(x - 1)^2$
c) $(x + \frac{1}{2})^2 + \frac{3}{4}$
d) $(x - 3)^2$
e) $(x - 3)^2 - 2$
f) $(x - 2)^2 - 4$
g) $(x + 1\frac{1}{2})^2 - 6\frac{1}{4}$
h) $(x - \frac{1}{2})^2 - 3\frac{1}{4}$
i) $(x - 5)^2$
j) $(x - 5)^2 - 25$
k) $(x + 4)^2 + 1$
l) $(x - 6)^2 - 1$

Q2 a) $x = 0.30, x = -3.30$
b) $x = 2.30, x = -1.30$
c) $x = 0.65, x = -4.65$
d) $x = 0.62, x = -1.62$
e) $x = 4.19, x = -1.19$
f) $x = 2.82, x = 0.18$
g) $x = 1.46, x = -0.46$
h) $x = 2.15, x = -0.15$

Algebra Crossword

Simultaneous Equations P.63

Q1 a) $x = 4, y = 18$ OR $x = -3, y = 11$

b) $x = 6, y = 28$ OR $x = -3, y = 1$

c) $x = 1.5, y = 4.5$ OR $x = -1, y = 2$

d) $x = -3, y = 33/5$ OR $x = 2, y = \dfrac{28}{5}$

e) $x = -\frac{1}{4}, y = \frac{17}{4}$ OR $x = -3, y = 40$

f) $x = -\frac{2}{3}, y = \frac{31}{3}$ OR $x = -4, y = 57$

Q2 **a)** $x = 1, y = 2$

b) $x = 0, y = 3$

c) $x = -1\frac{1}{2}, y = 4$

d) $x = 5, y = 23$ OR $x = -2, y = 2$

e) $x = \frac{1}{3}, y = -\frac{29}{3}$ OR $x = 4, y = 38$

f) $x = \frac{1}{2}, y = -\frac{3}{2}$ OR $x = -2, y = 6$

g) $x = 1, y = 9$

h) $x = 8, y = -\frac{1}{2}$

i) $x = -1, y = 3$

Q3 **a)** $6x + 5y = 430$
$4x + 10y = 500$
b) $x = 45, y = 32$

Q4 7 chickens, 4 cats

Q5 5 g (jellies are 4 g)

Q6 $3y + 2x = 18$
$y + 3x = 6$ .... $x = 0, y = 6$

$4y + 5x = 7$
$2x - 3y = 12$ .... $x = 3, y = -2$

$4x - 6y = 13$
$x + y = 2$ .... $x = 2\frac{1}{2}, y = -\frac{1}{2}$

Q7 $5m + 2c = 344$
$4m + 3c = 397$ .... $m = 34p, c = 87p$

Q8 $x = 12, y = 2$

Number Sequences P.64

Q1 **a)** 9, 11, 13, add 2 each time
b) 32, 64, 128, multiply by 2 each time
c) 30000, 300000, 3000000, multiply by 10 each time
d) 19, 23, 27, add 4 each time
e) -6, -11, -16, take 5 off each time

Q2 **a)** 4, 7, 10, 13, 16
b) 3, 8, 13, 18, 23
c) 1, 4, 9, 16, 25
d) -2, 1, 6, 13, 22

Q3 **a)** $2n$ **b)** $2n - 1$
c) $5n$ **d)** $3n + 2$

Q4 **a)** 19, 22, 25, $3n + 4$
b) 32, 37, 42, $5n + 7$
c) 46, 56, 66, $10n - 4$
d) 82, 89, 96, $7n + 47$

X and Y Coordinates P.65

Q1

missing coordinate = (5,3)

Q2

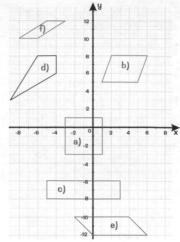

a) B is (1, -3)   **b)** C is (5, 5)
c) A is (-5, -8)   **d)** D is (-4, 6)
e) D is (0, -12)   **f)** C is (-3, 12)

Q3

C = (2, 1), D = (2, -2)

Straight Line Graphs P.66-P.67

Q1 **a)** B   **f)** F
b) A   **g)** C
c) F   **h)** B
d) G   **i)** D
e) E   **j)** H

Q2

x	-4	-3	-2	-1	0	1	2	3	4
3x	-12	-9	-6	-3	0	3	6	9	12
-1	-1	-1	-1	-1	-1	-1	-1	-1	-1
y	-13	-10	-7	-4	-1	2	5	8	11

Q3

x	-6	-4	-2	0	2	4	6
½ x	-3	-2	-1	0	1	2	3
-3	-3	-3	-3	-3	-3	-3	-3
y	-6	-5	-4	-3	-2	-1	0

Q4

x	0	3	8
y	3	9	19

a) 13   **c)** 4
b) 7   **d)** 7

Q5

x	-8	-4	8
y	-5	-4	-1

a) -2   **c)** 4
b) -3   **d)** 6

Q6

Number of Units used	0	100	200	300
Cost using method A	10	35	60	85
Cost using method B	40	45	50	55

a) i) £27.50   **ii)** £43.50
b) Method A
c) 150 units

---

y = mx + c P.68-P.69

Q1 **a)** $m = 4, (0, 3)$
b) $m = 3, (0, -2)$
c) $m = 2, (0, 1)$
d) $m = -3, (0, 3)$
e) $m = 5, (0, 0)$
f) $m = -2, (0, 3)$
g) $m = -6, (0, -4)$
h) $m = 1, (0, 0)$

i) $m = -\frac{1}{2}, (0, 3)$

j) $m = \frac{1}{4}, (0, 2)$

k) $m = \frac{4}{3}, (0, 2)$

l) $m = -\frac{5}{2}, (0, -2)$

m) $m = \frac{1}{2}, (0, -\frac{3}{2})$

n) $m = \frac{7}{3}, (0, \frac{5}{3})$

Answers: P.69 — P.73

o) $m = -1, (0, 0)$
p) $m = 1, (0, 0)$
q) $m = 1, (0, 3)$
r) $m = 1, (0, -3)$
s) $m = 3, (0, 7)$
t) $m = 5, (0, 3)$
u) $m = -2, (0, -3)$
v) $m = 2, (0, 4)$

Q2
a) $-\frac{1}{2}$ **h)** 1
b) 3 **i)** -1
c) $-\frac{1}{4}$ **j)** $\frac{1}{3}$
d) -2 **k)** $-\frac{1}{2}$
e) $-\frac{2}{3}$ **l)** 3
f) $-\frac{8}{3}$ **m)** 4
g) 4

Q3
a) 2 **d)** -2
b) $\frac{1}{2}$ **e)** $\frac{1}{2}$
c) -1 **f)** $-\frac{3}{4}$

Q4 The gradient is -0.23 so it's a blue run.

Q5
a) $y = \frac{7}{2}x - 1$ **d)** $y = \frac{1}{4}x - 3$
b) $y = \frac{1}{2}x + 4$ **e)** $y = -\frac{1}{2}x$
c) $y = -\frac{1}{5}x + 7$ **f)** $y = -2x - 6$

Q6
a) $y = x + 4$ **c)** $y = -x$
b) $y = 3x + 2$ **d)** $y = -3x + 4$

Q7
a) $y = x$
b) $y = 3x$
c) $y = 2x + 1$

Q8

c) $y = -3x + 2.5$
b) $y = \frac{1}{2}x + 5$
a) $y = 2x - 1$

Q9
a) $x = 4$ **c)** $y = 7$
b) $x = 8$ **d)** $y = 9$

Q10 $(7, 20)$ and $(5, 14)$

D/T Graphs and V/T Graphs P.70-P.71

Q1
a) 4 km
b) 15 mins and 45 mins
c) 2.4 km/h
d) 1100
e) 10 km/h
f) 1030

Q2
a) 85 mins
b) 80 mins
c) 16.9 mph
d) 57.6 mph
e) No, because the total driving time is 80 minutes.

Q3

He waited for 5 mins.

Q4
a) A 80.0 km/h, fastest.
B 57.1 km/h
C 66.7 km/h
D 44.4 km/h
E 50.0 km/h
b) steepest slope was fastest, least steep slope was slowest.

Q5
a) B   **b)** 3¾ mins
c) B
d) i) 267 m/min   **ii)** 16.0 km/h
e) C was the fastest; 700 m/min or 42 km/h

Q6
a)

b) accept 1243-1245
c) accept 35-36 km

Q7
a)

b) 25.75 km   **c)** 3.68 km/h
d) Her fastest speed was in the first section (steepest graph) — her speed was 5.14 km/h.

Inequalities P.72-P.73

Q1
a) $9 \le x < 13$
b) $-4 \le x < 1$
c) $x \ge -4$
d) $x < 5$
e) $x > 25$
f) $-1 < x \le 3$
g) $0 < x \le 5$
h) $x < -2$

Q2
a)
b)
c)
d)
e)

Q3
f)
g)
h)

Q3
a)
b)
c)
d)
e)
f)
g)
h)

Q4
a) $x > 3$ **b)** $x < 4$
c) $x \le 5$ **d)** $x \le 6$
e) $x \ge 7.5$ **f)** $x < 4$
g) $x < 7$ **h)** $x < 4$
i) $x \ge 3$ **j)** $x > 11$
k) $x < 3$ **l)** $x \ge -½$
m) $x \le -2$ **n)** $x > 5$
o) $x < 15$ **p)** $x \ge -2$

Q5 Largest integer for x is 2.

Q6 $\frac{11 - x}{2} < 5, x > 1$

Q7 $1130 \le 32x$
36 classrooms are needed.

Q8 50 guests (including bride and groom), $900 \ge 18x$

Q9 $x \ge 2$, $y > 1$, $x + y \le 5$

Q10

Q11

Q12 a) $x > 5$, $y \ge 7, x + y \ge 14$
b)

Answers: P.74 — P.79

Unit 3 — Geometry and Algebra
Graphs to Recognise P.74-P.76

Q1
a) Cubic	**b)** Straight Line
c) Reciprocal	**d)** Quadratic
e) Cubic	**f)** Reciprocal
g) Quadratic	**h)** Quadratic
i) Straight Line	**j)** Cubic
k) Cubic	**l)** Quadratic

Q2
a) — xviii)	**l)** — xvii)
b) — x)	**m)** — xiv)
c) — ix)	**n)** — xxi)
d) — iv)	**o)** — viii)
e) — ii)	**p)** — xvi)
f) — xv)	**q)** — vi)
g) — xiii)	**r)** — xix)
h) — xi)	**s)** — v)
i) — i)	**t)** — iii)
j) — vii)	**u)** — xii)
k) — xx)	

Quadratic Graphs P.77

Q1

x	-4	-3	-2	-1	0	1	2	3	4
$y=2x^2$	32	18	8	2	0	2	8	18	32

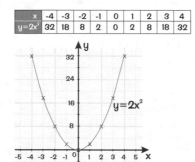

Q2

x	-4	-3	-2	-1	0	1	2	3	4
x^2	16	9	4	1	0	1	4	9	16
$y=x^2+x$	12	6	2	0	0	2	6	12	20

Q3 **a)**

x	-4	-3	-2	-1	0	1	2	3	4
3	3	3	3	3	3	3	3	3	3
$-x^2$	-16	-9	-4	-1	-0	-1	-4	-9	-16
$y=3-x^2$	-13	-6	-1	2	3	2	-1	-6	-13

b)

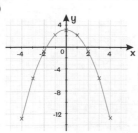

c) 3

Cubic Graphs P.78

Q1

x	-3	-2	-1	0	1	2	3
$y=x^3$	-27	-8	-1	0	1	8	27

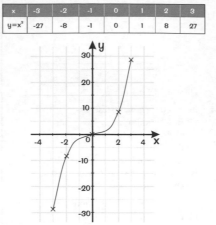

Q2

x	-3	-2	-1	0	1	2	3
$y=-x^3$	27	8	1	0	-1	-8	-27

Q3

x	-3	-2	-1	0	1	2	3
x^3	-27	-8	-1	0	1	8	27
+4	4	4	4	4	4	4	4
y	-23	-4	3	4	5	12	31

Q4

x	-3	-2	-1	0	1	2	3
$-x^3$	27	8	1	0	-1	-8	-27
-4	-4	-4	-4	-4	-4	-4	-4
y	23	4	-3	-4	-5	-12	-31

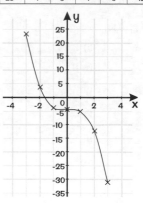

Q5 The graph has been moved 4 units up the *y*-axis.

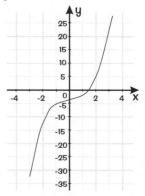

Q6 The graph has been moved 4 units down the *y*-axis.

Simultaneous Equations and Graphs P.79

Q1
a) $x=3, y=3$	**b)** $x=2, y=5$
c) $x=1, y=2$	**d)** $x=1, y=2$
e) $x=1, y=4$	**f)** $x=1, y=2$
g) $x=2, y=3$	**h)** $x=2, y=3$
i) $x=5, y=2$	**j)** $x=3, y=4$

Q2
a) $x=0, x=1$
b) $x=2.7, x=-0.7$
c) $x=3.4, x=-2.4$
d) $x=1.6, x=-2.6$
e) $x=0.7$
f) $x=3.4, x=-2.4$
g) $x=1.6, x=-2.6$

Q3

x	-4	-3	-2	-1	0	1	2	3	4
$-\frac{1}{2}x^2$	-8	-4.5	-2	-0.5	0	-0.5	-2	-4.5	-8
+5	5	5	5	5	5	5	5	5	5
y	-3	0.5	3	4.5	5	4.5	3	0.5	-3

a) $x = 3.2, x = -3.2$
b) $x = 4, x = -4$
c) $x = 2.3, x = -4.3$

The Quadratic Formula P.80-P.81

Q1
a) 1.87, 0.13
b) 2.39, 0.28
c) 1.60, - 3.60
d) 1.16, -3.16
e) 0.53, -4.53
f) -11.92, -15.08
g) -2.05, -4.62
h) 0.84, 0.03

Q2
a) -2, -6   b) 0.67, -0.5
c) 3, -2   d) 2, 1
e) 3, 0.75   f) 3, 0
g) 0.67   h) 0, -2.67
i) 4, -0.5   j) 4, -5
k) 1, -3   l) 5, -1.33
m) 1.5, -1   n) -2.5, 1
o) 0.5, 0.33   p) 1, -3
q) 2, -6   r) 2, -4

Q3
a) 0.30, -3.30   b) 3.65, -1.65
c) 0.62, -1.62   d) -0.55, -5.45
e) -0.44, -4.56   f) 1.62, -0.62
g) 0.67, -4.00   h) -0.59, -3.41
i) 7.12, -1.12   j) 13.16, 0.84
k) 1.19, -4.19   l) 1.61, 0.53
m) 0.44, -3.44   n) 2.78, 0.72

Q4
a) 1.7, -4.7   b) -0.27, -3.73
c) 1.88, -0.88   d) 0.12, -4.12
e) 4.83, -0.83   f) 1.62, -0.62
g) 1.12, -1.79   h) -0.21, -4.79
i) 2.69, -0.19   j) 2.78, 0.72
k) 1, 0   l) 1.5, 0.50

Q5 $x^2 - 3.6x + 3.24 = 0$
$x = 1.8$

Q6 a) $x^2 + 2.5x - 144.29 = 0$
$x = 10.83$
b) 48.3 cm

Trial and Improvement P.82

Q1

Guess (x)	value of x^3+x	Too large or too small
2	$2^3+2=10$	Too small
3	$3^3+3=30$	Too large
2.8	$(2.8)^3+2.8=20.2$	Too small
2.7	$(2.7)^3+2.7=22.4$	Too small
2.9	$(2.9)^3+2.9=24.0$	Too large
2.75	$(2.75)^3+2.75=23.5$	Too small

∴ To 1 d.p the solution is x=2.8

Q2

Guess (x)	value of x^3+x^2-4x	Too large or too small
-3	$(-3)^3 + (-3)^2 - 4(-3) = -6$	Too small
-2	$(-2)^3 + (-2)^2 - 4(-2) = 4$	Too large
-2.1	$(-2.1)^3 + (-2.1)^2 - 4(-2.1) = 3.549$	Too large
-2.2	$(-2.2)^3 + (-2.2)^2 - 4(-2.2) = 2.99$	Too small
-2.15	$(-2.15)^3 + (-2.15)^2 - 4(-2.15) = 3.3$	Too large

∴ To 1 d.p the solution is x=−2.2

Guess (x)	value of x^3+x^2-4x	Too large or too small
-1	$-1 +1 +4 = 4$	Too large
0	$0 + 0 - 0 = 0$	Too small
-0.8	$(-0.8)^3 + (-0.8)^2 - 4(-0.8) = 3.328$	Too small
-0.7	$(-0.7)^3 + (-0.7)^2 - 4(-0.7) = 2.947$	Too small
-0.75	$(-0.75)^3 + (-0.75)^2 - 4(-0.75) = 3.141$	Too large

∴ To 1 d.p the solution is x=−0.7

Guess (x)	value of x^3+x^2-4x	Too large or too small
1	$1 + 1 - 4 = -2$	Too large
2	$8 + 4 - 8 = 4$	Too large
1.9	$(1.9)^3 + (1.9)^2 - 4(1.9) = 2.869$	Too small
1.95	$(1.95)^3 + (1.95)^2 - 4(1.95) = 3.417$	Too large

∴ To 1 d.p the solution is x=1.9

Q3 Try different values of x to 1 d.p. between 3 and 4 to see which gives the highest value of V, e.g:

Guess (x)	value of $4x^3-80x^2+400x$
3	108-720+1200 = 588
4	256-1280+1600 = 576
3.5	171.5-980+1400 = 591.5
3.4	157.216-924.8+1360 = 592.416
3.3	143.748-871.2+1320 = 592.548
3.2	131.072-819.2+1280 = 591.872

∴ To 1 d.p the solution is x=3.3

Direct and Inverse Proportion P.83-P.85

Q1 £247.80
Q2 112 hours
Q3 £96.10
Q4 a) $9\frac{1}{3}$ cm
b) 30.45 km
Q5 $y = 20$
Q6 $y = 1.8$
Q7 $y = 184.8$
Q8 $x = 75$
Q9

X	2	4	6
Y	5	10	15

X	3	6	9
Y	4.5	9	13.5

X	27	54	81
Y	5	10	15

Q10 $y = 2$
Q11 $x = 2$
Q12 a) $x = 4$
b) $y = 6$
Q13 1.8 hrs or 1 h 48 min
Q14

x	1	2	3	4	5	6
y	48	24	16	12	9.6	8

Q15 a) 78.5 cm²
b) 3.0 cm
Q16 $y = 36$
Q17 a) $k = 1.6$
b) $y = 819.2$
c) $x = 11.5$
Q18

x	1	2	5	10
y	100	25	4	1

x	2	4	6	8
y	24	6	2⅔	1.5

Q19 4 kg
Q20 a) $r = 96$ b) $s = 4$
c) $r = 600$ d) $s = -8$
Q21 9.5 N kg⁻¹
Q22 $y \propto \dfrac{1}{x}$
a) $y = \dfrac{200}{x}$
b) $y = 31.25$
c) $x = 12.5$

Symmetry P.86

Q1

a) b) c)
d) e) f)

Q2 a) 6   b) 8
c) 5   d) 3

Q3

M H V B
1 2 1 1

Order of Rotation

A K Z
1 1 2

Q4 a)

Order of Rotation = 3

b)
Order of Rotation = 1

c)
Order of Rotation = 2

d)

Order of Rotation = 1

Answers: P.87 — P.92

e)

Order of Rotation = 8

f)

Order of Rotation = 2

Perimeters and Areas P.87-P.88

Q1 Area 24 cm², perimeter 20 cm

Q2 Area 25 cm², perimeter 20 cm

Q3 **a)** Area = $(4 \times 4) - (1 \times 2 + \frac{1}{2} \times \pi \times 1^2) + \frac{1}{2} \times \pi \times 2^2$

= 16 − 3.5708 + 6.2832

= 18.7 m² (1 d.p.)

b) Three 1 litre tins of paint are needed for two coats.

c) Perimeter = $1 + 1 + (\frac{1}{2} \times \pi \times 2)$

$+ 1 + 1 + 4 + (\frac{1}{2} \times \pi \times 4) + 4$

$= 12 + 3\pi = 21.4$ m (1 d.p.)

Q4 **a)** l = 24, w = 12, area = 288 m²

b) 1 Carpet tile = 0.50 × 0.50 = 0.25 m²
So 288 m² ÷ 0.25 = 1152 tiles are required.

c) £4.99 per m² => £4.99 for 4 tiles
Total cost = (1152 ÷ 4) × 4.99 = £1437.12

Q5 Area = 120 cm²

Q6 Each square = 0.6 m × 0.6 m = 0.36 m².
Total area of material = 6 × 0.36 = 2.16 m².

Q7 Perimeter = $4 \times \sqrt{9000}$
= 379.47 m (2 d.p.)
Natasha ran: 11 × 379.47
= 4200 m (to nearest 100 m)

Q8 48 ÷ 5 = 9.6 m length. Area of 1 roll = 11 m × 0.5 m = 5.5 m².
48 m² ÷ 5.5 m² = $8\frac{8}{11}$ rolls of turf required.
Of course 9 should be ordered.

Q9 Base length = 4773 ÷ 43 = 111 mm.

Q10 Area of metal blade = ½ × 35 × (70 + 155) = 3937.5 mm²

Q11 Area of larger triangle = ½ × 14.4 × 10 = 72 cm².
Area of inner triangle = ½ × 5.76 × 4 = 11.52 cm².
Area of metal used for a bracket = 72 − 11.52 = 60.48 cm².
So the bracket is too heavy.

Q12 T₁: ½ × 8 × 16 = 64 m²
Tr₁: ½ × 8 × (8 + 16) = 96 m²
Tr₂: ½ × 4 × (8 + 12) = 40 m²
T₂: ½ × 8 × 12 = 48 m²
Total area of glass sculpture = 248 m²

Q13 Area = ½ × 8.2 × 4.1 = 16.81 m²
Perimeter = 10.8 + 4.5 + 8.2 = 23.5 m.

Q14 **a)** Area of each isosceles triangle = ½ × 2.3 × 3.2 = 3.68 m²

b) Area of each side = $(\sqrt{3.2^2 + 1.15^2}) \times 4 = 13.6$ m²
Groundsheet = 2.3 × 4 = 9.2 m²

c) Total material = 2 × 3.68 + 9.2 + 2 × 13.6 = 43.8 m²

Q15

5.5 km
3.5 km
5.5 km
3.5 km

Area = ½ × product of diagonals
= ½ × 7 × 11 = 38.5 km².

Solids and Nets P.89-P.90

Q1

Base
X   X
F
Y

Q2

3 cm
2 cm   2 cm   3 cm
Base
4 cm

Other arrangements are possible.

Q3

Base
3 cm

Q4

Q5 **a)** Rectangle.
b) AH, CF, BG.
c) DF, AG, BH.   **d)** HC, BE, AF.
e) 8

Q6 **a)** 1   **b)** 1

Q7 **a)** 12   **b)** 7
c) 7

Q8 **a)** H, F and D
b) Line symmetry through lines AF, DH, BG and CE. Rotational symmetry of order 4.
c) 5 faces and vertices, 8 edges.

Q9 **a)** I   **b)** 64 cm²
c) 64 × 6 = 384 cm²
d)

Q10 E.g.

Q11 Net B

Q12 **a)** Front elevation:

5 m   3 m   3 m
4 m   4 m
or

b) Side elevation:

3 m   5 m   3 m
4 m   4 m
or

c) Plan:

4 m
4 m

Surface Area and Volume P.91-P.93

Q1 **a)** $\frac{1}{2}\pi(0.35)^2 = 0.192$ m²

b) 0.1924 × 3 = 0.577 m³

Q2 **a)** $\pi(2.5^2 - 2^2) = 7.07$ m²
£16 × 7.07 = £113.12 = £110 to nearest £10.

b) Volume = $\pi(2)^2 \times 0.50 = 6.28$ m³
so use 6.28 × 15 = 94 ml treatment to the nearest ml.

Q3 **a)** Volume Cube = Volume Cylinder
$10^3 = \pi r^2 \times 10$ so $r^2 = \frac{10^2}{\pi}$,
r = 5.64 cm

b) S.A. of cylinder = $2\pi rh + 2\pi r^2$ = $2\pi \times 5.64... \times 10 + 2\pi \times (5.64...)^2$
= 554.49 cm².

Q4 **a)** $\pi(5)^2(16) = 1257$ cm³

b) $\pi(5)^2 h = 600$
$h = \frac{600}{25\pi} = 7.64$ cm

Q5 $(3)(3)(0.5) - \pi(0.7)^2(0.5) = 3.73$ cm³

Q6 **a)**

Depth
Time

b)

Depth
Time

Q7 $(\pi \times (2)^2 \times 110) + (\frac{1}{2}(14 + 20) \times 6 \times 20) = 3422.30$ cm³
2 × 3422.30 = 6844.60 cm³ = 6.84 l

Q8 **a)** (60)(30) + (30)(120) = 5400 cm²

b) 5400 × 100 = 540000 cm³ = 0.54 m³

Q9 **a) i)** B = (0, 8, 5)   **ii)** D = (4, 8, 0)

b) (½ × 4 × 5) × 8 = 80 units³

Q10 $AB^2 = 2^2 + 1.5^2$ $AB = 2.5$ m
1 panel on roof $= \frac{1}{2}AB \times \frac{5}{2}$
$= 1.25 \times 2.5 = 3.125$ m²
Front of greenhouse $= (2.5 \times 4) + (\frac{1}{2} \times 4 \times 1.5) = 13$ m²
Total $= 3.125 + 13 = 16.125$ m²

Q11 a) $\frac{1}{2}(\frac{4}{3}\pi(1.3)^3) + \pi(1.3)^2 \times 1.8$
$+ \frac{1}{3}\pi(1.3)^2 \times 1.2 = 16.28$ cm³

b) Volume of sand in hemisphere and cone parts remain the same so change is in cylindrical part. Therefore $h + 0.3 = 1.8$, $h = 1.5$ cm.

c) Volume of sand transferred $= \frac{1}{2}(\frac{4}{3}\pi(1.3)^3) + \pi(1.3)^2 \times 1.5$
$= 12.57$ cm³
Time Taken $= \frac{12.57}{0.05} \approx 251$ secs.
$= 4$ minutes 11 secs.

Q12 a) Volume of ice cream
$= \frac{1}{3}\pi(R^2H - r^2h) + \frac{1}{2}(\frac{4}{3}\pi R^3)$
$= \frac{1}{3}\pi(2.5^2 \times 10 - 1^2 \times 4)$
$+ \frac{1}{2}(\frac{4}{3}\pi \times 2.5^3)$
$= 93.99$ cm³ of ice cream.

b) Outer surface area of cone
$= \pi Rl$
Using pythagoras,
$l^2 = 10^2 + 2.5^2 = 106.25$,
$l = 10.3$ cm. So S.A. $= \pi \times 2.5 \times 10.3 = 81.0$ cm².

Q13 Vol. increase is a cylinder of height 4.5 cm. So vol. increase $= \pi(5)^2 \times 4.5 = 353.4$ cm³.
Volume of each marble $= \frac{353.4}{200} = 1.767$ cm³
$\frac{4}{3}\pi r^3 = 1.767 \Rightarrow r = 0.75$ cm

Q14 a) $x(3-x)(5-x)$ m³ or $x^3 - 8x^2 + 15x$

b)

X	0	1	2	3
V	0	8	6	0

c)

d) about 8.2 m³

e) ends $2(1.2)(1.8) =$ 4.32
$+$
side faces $2(1.2)(3.8) =$ 9.12
$+$
tops $2(3.8)(1.8) =$ 13.68
So area is about   27.12 m²

f) $x = 2$ or $x = 0.6$
If $x = 0.6$:
ends $2(0.6)(2.4) =$ 2.88 +
side faces $2(0.6)(4.4) =$ 5.28 +
tops $2(2.4)(4.4) =$ 21.12
                    29.28 m²

If $x = 2$:
ends $2(2)(1) =$ 4 +
side faces $2(2)(3) =$ 12 +
tops $2(1)(3) =$ 6
                    22 m²
Maximum Total S.A. ≈ 29.28 m²

Length, Area and Volume Formulas P.94

Q1 a) Length.   **b)** Area.
c) None of these.
d) Length.   **e)** Volume.
f) Volume.   **g)** Volume.
h) None of these.

Q2 a) Length.   **b)** Length.
c) Area.   **d)** Length.

Q3 a) None of these.
b) Perimeter.   **c)** Area.
d) Area.

Q4 No. (It has an r missing for it to be the volume of a sphere.)

Q5 Yes. (It is the formula for the area of a triangle.)

Q6 Yes. (It is the formula for the area of a trapezium.)

Q7 Yes. (It could be the perimeter of a symmetrical irregular pentagon.)

Q8 No. (It is only a length × a length. In fact it is the formula for the area of a kite.)

Q9 a) Volume of a cube $= l^3$.
b) Area of a circle $= \pi(d/2)^2$.
c) Perimeter of a circle $= 2\pi r$.

Geometry P.95-P.96

Q1 a) $x = 47°$ **b)** $y = 154°$
c) $z = 22°$ **d)** $p = 35°, q = 45°$

Q2 a) $a = 146°$
b) $m = 131°, z = 48°$
c) $x = 68°, p = 112°$
d) $s = 20°, t = 90°$

Q3 a) $x = 96°, p = 38°$
b) $a = 108°, b = 23°, c = 95°$
c) $d = 120°, e = 60°, f = 60°, g = 120°$
d) $h = 155°, i = 77.5°, j = 102.5°, k = 77.5°$

Q4 a) $b = 70°$ $c = 30°$
$d = 50°$ $e = 60°$
$f = 150°$
b) $g = 21°$ $h = 71°$
$i = 80°$ $j = 38°$
$k = 92°$
c) $l = 35°$ $m = 145°$
$n = 55°$ $p = 125°$

Q5 a) $x = 162° y = 18°$
b) $x = 87°$ $y = 93°$
$z = 93°$
c) $a = 30°$ $2a = 60°$
$5a = 150°$ $4a = 120°$

Q6 a) $a = 141°, b = 141°, c = 39°, d = 141°, e = 39°$
b) $a = 47°, b = 47°, c = 133°, d = 43°, e = 43°$
c) $m = 140°, n = 140°, p = 134°, q = 46°, r = 40°$

Regular Polygons P.97-P.98

Q1 Isosceles.

Q2

interior angle $= 60°$

Q3

order of rotational symmetry $= 6$.

Q4 a) Angles at a point sum to 360°, hence m + m + r = 360°.
Angles in a pentagon sum to 540°. We know two angles are 90°, so we are left with 360°. The only angles left are m, m and r so m + m + r must equal 360°.
b) r°.
c)

Q5 a) $90° + 60° = 150°$

b)

$\angle PRW = 75°$
c) $180 - (360/n) = 150$
$180n - 360 = 150n$
$30n = 360 \Rightarrow n = 12$

Q6 $540° - (100° + 104° + 120°)$
$= 216°$ for two equal angles
$\therefore 1$ angle $= 108°$

Q7 a) Interior angle $= 165°$
b) Exterior angle $= 180° - 165° = 15°$
Sum of exterior angles $= 15 \times 24 = 360°$

Q8 a) $\frac{360}{5} = 72°$
b) $\frac{180 - 72}{2} = 54°$
c) i) $90°$ **ii)** $36°$
d) $36°$ (BAE is an isosceles triangle)

Q9 $(n-2)180 = 2520, n = 16$

Q10 a) $(\frac{360}{5}) \div 2 = 36°$

b) OX = 5 cos 36 = 4.045.
Hence MX = 5 – 4.045
= 0.95 cm.

Q11 a)

b) Angle CDE = angle DEF
$=\dfrac{(8-2)180}{8} = 135$

so angle EFC $=\dfrac{360-2(135)}{2} = 45$

or exterior angle = 45° = angle EFC,
alternate angles.

Circle Geometry P.99-P.101

Q1 a) 117.607 m²
b) 45.216 = 45 m to 2 s.f.
c) 46.5 m to 1dp.
d) 14.152 cm² to 3dp.

Q2 a) Area = area of a full circle radius
10 cm. A = πr^2 = 3.14 × 10²
= 314 cm².
Circumference = π × D = 3.14 × 20 =
62.8 cm. Perimeter = 62.8 + 20 = 82.8
cm

b) Area = (area of a full circle radius 15
cm) + (area of a rectangle 15 × 30 cm)
= (π × 15²) + (15 × 30)
= 1156.5 cm².
Perimeter = (Circumference of a full
circle radius 15 cm) + 15 +15 (two
shorter sides of rectangle) =
(π × 30) + 30 = 124.2 cm.

c) Area = Outer semi circle – Inner semi
circle = 510.25 m².
Perimeter = ½ Circumference of larger
+ ½ Circumference of inner + 5 + 5 = ½
× π × 70 + ½ × π × 60 + 10 = 214.1 m.

Q3 a) ABDC = $\dfrac{60}{360}$ × π(30)² – $\dfrac{60}{360}$ × π(20)²
= 261.8 mm²
b) 2(½π5²) = 78.5 mm².
Hence 261.8 + 78.5 = 340.3 mm².
c) $\frac{1}{6}\pi R^2$
d) $\frac{1}{6}\pi R^2 - \frac{1}{6}\pi r^2 = \frac{1}{6}\pi(R^2 - r^2)$
e) $\frac{1}{6}\pi(R^2 - r^2) + \pi(\frac{R-r}{2})^2$

Q4 a) 80/360 × π5² = 17.45 cm²
b) Area of triangle AOB =
$\frac{1}{2}$ × 5 × 5 × sin80 = 12.31 cm².
Shaded Area = 17.45 – 12.31
= 5.14 cm²

Q5 a) BAD = 80° (opposite angle C in cyclic
quadrilateral)
b) EAB = 180 – 80 – 30 = 70°

Q6 a) BD = 5 cm (as the tangents BD and CD
are equal).
b) Angle COD = 70° (= 180° – (20° +
90°)), since the tangent CD meets the
radius OC at an angle of 90°.
c) Angle COB = 140° (since angle BOD
equals angle COD).

d) Angle CAB = 70° (since the angle at
the centre (COB) is twice the angle at
the edge (CAB)).

Q7 a) BOE = 106° (angle at centre)
b) ACE = 32° (angle in opposite segment)

Q8 a) ACD = 70° (angle in opposite segment)
b) BAD = 180 – (30 + 70) = 80° (opposite
angles of a cyclic quadrilateral total
180°)

Q9 a) Angles in the same segment.
b) 3x + 40 = 6x – 50
90 = 3x
30 = x
angle ABD = 3(30) + 40 = 130°

Q10 There are 2 ways of answering this
question.

A diameter through O bisects the chord at
X so cos 20° $=\dfrac{AX}{5}$ =>
AX = 4.698 and
AB = 9.40 cm.

or by the sine rule $\dfrac{AB}{\sin 140} = \dfrac{5}{\sin 20}$
AB $= \dfrac{5\sin 140}{\sin 20}$ = 9.40 cm

Q11 a) Angle ABD = 70° (angle at centre = 2 ×
angle at circumference)
b) Angle ABC = 90° (angle in semicircle)
c) Angle DBC = 20° (90° – 70°)

Q12 a) 90° (angle in a semicircle)
b) The angle at A = 90° (tangent and
radius are perpendicular). The third
angle in the triangle is
180 – 90 – 23 = 67° and so
x = 90 – 67 = 23°.
Or, by opposite segment theorem:
x = angle ABC = 23°.

Q13 a) With AD as a chord, angle
ABD = ACD = 30° (same segment);
angle AXB = 85° (vertically opposite
angles). The third angles must be the
same in both triangles so the triangles
must be similar.

b) Ratio of lengths $= \dfrac{4}{8} = \dfrac{1}{2}$
so XB = 5 cm
c) angle BDC = 180 – 85 – 30 = 65°

Q14 a) 90° (angle in a semicircle)
b) Pythagoras is needed here but in the
form
AC² + 3² = 10²
AC² = 100 – 9 = 91
AC = 9.54 cm
c) AD = 5 cm so DC = 9.54 – 5
= 4.54 cm then Pythagoras again gives
(4.54)² + 3² = (DOB)²
20.606 + 9 = (DOB)²
So DOB = 5.44 cm

The Four Transformations
P.102-P.103

Q1 a) to **e)** — see diagram.

f) Rotation of 180°, centre (3, 0)

Q2 a), b), d), e) — see diagram

c) Rotation 180° about (0, 2).
f) 90° rotation anticlockwise
about $\left(-\frac{1}{2}, -\frac{1}{2}\right)$.

Q3 a), b) — see diagram.

c) Ratio of areas C:A = 1:4
Q4 a), b), c) — see diagram.

d) Rotation of 180° about (0, 0)

Q5 a)

b) $\overrightarrow{QO} = \left(\begin{smallmatrix}-3\\-4\end{smallmatrix}\right)$
$T = \left(\begin{smallmatrix}11\\8\end{smallmatrix}\right) + \left(\begin{smallmatrix}-3\\-4\end{smallmatrix}\right) = \left(\begin{smallmatrix}8\\4\end{smallmatrix}\right)$

see diagram

c) $\left(\begin{smallmatrix}-1\\2\end{smallmatrix}\right) + \left(\begin{smallmatrix}8\\4\end{smallmatrix}\right) + \left(\begin{smallmatrix}-3\\-4\end{smallmatrix}\right) + \left(\begin{smallmatrix}-4\\-2\end{smallmatrix}\right) = \left(\begin{smallmatrix}0\\0\end{smallmatrix}\right)$

Answers: P.104 — P.108

Congruence, Similarity and Enlargement P.104-P.105

Q1 ABC and DEF are congruent — two sides and the angle between them are the same in both triangles.

Q2 **a)** Angle A shared. Parallel lines make corresponding angles equal so the triangles are similar.

b) Ratio of lengths given by $\frac{AB}{AD} = \frac{12}{20} = \frac{3}{5}$

So $x = 25 \times \frac{3}{5} = 15$ cm

Also $\frac{y+10}{y} = \frac{5}{3}$

=> $2y = 30$, $y = 15$ cm

Q3

Hence 7 ways to draw <u>another</u>.

Q4 Widths in ratio 2:3, so volumes in ratio 8:27.
Volume = $30 \times \frac{27}{8} = 101$ litres

Q5 **a)** All lengths must be enlarged in the same ratio for them to be similar.
b) 4 litres

Q6 **a)** Triangles APQ and STC (both isosceles and share either angle A or C)

b) Ratio AC:AQ = 24:7.5 = 3.2:1 so AP =
$15 \times \frac{1}{3.2} = 4.6875$ cm
PT = $24 - 2 (4.6875)$
= 14.625 cm.

c) Using $\frac{1}{2}$(base)(height)
$= \frac{1}{2}(24)(9) = 108$ cm²

d) Scale factor = $\frac{1}{3.2}$
Area scale factor = $\frac{1}{10.24}$
Area of triangle APQ = $108 \times \frac{1}{10.24}$
= 10.5 cm²

e) $108 - 2 (10.5) = 87$ cm²

Q7 **a)** 2 end faces $2 \times (2 \times 3) = 12$ cm²
2 side faces $2 \times (5 \times 3)$
$= 30$ cm²
Top & bottom $2 \times (5 \times 2)$
$= 20$ cm²
Total = 62 cm²
b) SF for length = 1:4
SF for area = 1:16
new area = 62×16
= 992 cm²

Q8 **a)** & **b)**

c) triangle $A_2B_2C_2$

Q9 **a)** volume $- \frac{1}{3}\pi(100^2)(100)$
$= 1047198$ cm³
$= 1.05$ m³

b) 50 cm
c) ratio = $1:2^3 = 1:8$
d) Volume of small cone =
$1.05 \times \frac{1}{8} = 0.131$ m³
e) volume of portion left =
$1.05 - 0.131 = 0.919$
so ratio = $0.919:0.131 = \frac{0.919}{0.131}:1$
= 7:1

Pythagoras and Bearings P.106-P.107

Q1 **a)** 10.8 cm   **f)** 7.89 m
b) 6.10 m   **g)** 9.60 cm
c) 5 cm   **h)** 4.97 m
d) 27.0 mm   **i)** 6.80 cm
e) 8.49 m   **j)** 8.5 m

Q2 a = 3.32 cm   f = 8.62 m
b = 6 cm   g = 6.42 m
c = 6.26 m   h = 19.2 mm
d = 5.6 mm   i = 9.65 m
e = 7.08 mm   j = 48.7 mm

Q3 k = 6.55 cm   q = 7.07 cm
l = 4.87 m   r = 7.50 m
m = 6.01 m   s = 9.45 mm
n = 12.4 cm   t = 4.33 cm
p = 5.22 cm   u = 7.14 m

Q4 **a)** 245°   **b)** 310°
c) 035°   **d)** 131°
e) 297°, 028°, 208°
f) 139°, 284°

Q5 9.7 m

Q6 314 m

Q7 **a)** 12 cm, 7.94 cm
b) 40.9 cm
c) 89.7 cm²

Q8 192 km

Q9 **a)**

i) 268 m
ii) 225 m
b) $350^2 = 122\,500$.
$225^2 + 268^2 = 122\,449$

Q10

a) 96 km
b) 255 km
c) 266 km
d) 156°
e) 082°
f) 177°

Q11

2500 m, 010°

Q12

13.9 km from the starting point.
150° to return to base.

Trigonometry P.108-P.110

		(tan)	(sin)	(cos)
Q1	**a)**	0.306	0.292	0.956
	b)	8.14	0.993	0.122
	c)	0.0875	0.0872	0.996
	d)	0.532	0.469	0.883
	e)	1	0.707	0.707

Q2 a = 1.40 cm
b = 6 cm
θ = 28.1°
c = 5.31 cm
d = 10.8 cm

Q3 e = 12.6 cm
f = 11.3 cm
θ = 49.5°
g = 6.71 m
h = 30.1 cm

Q4 i = 4.89 cm
j = 3.79 cm
θ = 52.4°
k = 5.32 cm
l = 41.6 cm

Q5 m = 11.3 cm
n = 18.8 cm
p = 8.62 cm
q = 21.3 cm
r = 54.6°
t = 59.8 cm
u = 14.5 cm
v = 11.7 cm
w = 11.7 cm

Q6 **a)**

b) 36.9°

Answers: P.109 — P.114

Q7 a)

b) 59.0°
c) 31.0°

Q8 a)

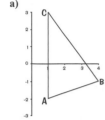

b) 71.6°
c) 36.9°
d) 71.5°

Q9   2.1 m

Q10   62°

Q11   20.5°

Q12

θ = 52.1°, bearing = 322°

Q13 a) both 30.8 cm
b) 27.5 cm **c)**   385 cm²

Q14

height = 5.90, base = 7.52,
so area = 22.2 cm².

Q15 a) 8.23 cm
b) 4.75 cm **c)**   39.1 cm²

Q16 a) 10.8 cm
b) 150.8 cm²   **c)** 21.0°

Q17

750 m

Q18

25.8 m

Q19

80 m

a) 102.4 m, 69.5 m
b) 32.9 m

Q20

86.6 km

3D Pythagoras and Trigonometry
P.111

Q1   B (1, 5, 8), C (4, 5, 8), D (4, 2, 8)
   E (4, 2, 3), F (1, 2, 3), G (1, 5, 3)

Q2 a) 59.0°
b) 23.3 cm
c) 25 cm
d) 21.1°

Q3 a) 42.5 cm
b) 50.9 cm

Q4 a) 36.1 cm, 21.5 cm, 31.0 cm
b) 36.9 cm

Q5 a) 15.4 cm
b) 20.4 cm

Q6   The 85p box

Q7 a) 3.82 cm
b) 45.8 cm²
c) 137.5 cm³

The Sine and Cosine Rules
P.112-P.114

Q1	$a = 4.80$ cm	$f = 5.26$ cm
	$b = 25.8$ mm	$g = 9.96$ cm
	$c = 13.0$ cm	$h = 20.2$ mm
	$d = 8.89$ m	$i = 3.72$ m
	$e = 18.4$ cm	$j = 8.29$ cm

Q2	$k = 51°$	$r = 64°$
	$l = 46°$	$s = 18°$
	$m = 43°$	$t = 49°$
	$p = 45°$	$u = 88°$
	$q = 36°$	

Q3	$a = 63°$	$i = 5.0$ mm
	$b = 45°$	$j = 68°$
	$c = 8.9$ cm	$k = 203$ mm
	$d = 27°$	$l = 127$ mm
	$e = 10.5$ cm	$m = 24.1$ cm
	$g = 49°$	$n = 149°$
	$h = 78°$	$p = 16°$

Q4 a) 46°
b) 52°   **c)** 82°

Q5   12.0 m

Q6 a) 28.8 km   **b)** 295.5°

Q7

base = 7.04 cm

base = 8.39 cm

Q8

Diagonals 11.2 cm and 6.6 cm.

Q9

Distance = 1.2 miles.
The alarm should be ringing because the
planes are less than 3 miles apart, so the
software seems reliable.

Q10 a) 16.9 m
b) 12.4 m
c) 25.8 m
d) 19.5 m

Q11

a) 86°
b) 323 km
c) 215°

Q12 a)

8 cm
60°
5.5 cm
7.1 cm

b)

7 cm   118.5°
8 cm

14.5 cm
(118.5° comes from the fact that the
minute hand is at 19.75 mins.
19.75 ÷ 60 × 360 = 118.5.)

c)

13.5 cm

Q13 Height of building = 35 m

Q14

Mary's string = 5.85 m
Jane's string = 7.13 m

The Graphs of Sin and Cos
P.115-P.116

Q1 A(180,0)
B(90,1)   C(−90,−1)

Q2 D(270,0)   F(0,1)
E(90,0)   G(−90,0)

Q3 A $y = \sin(x)$ B $y = \cos(x)$
C $y = \cos(x)$ D $y = \sin(x)$
E $y = \sin(x)$ F neither
G $y = \sin(x)$ H $y = \cos(x)$
I $y = \sin(x)$ J $y = \cos(x)$

Q4

$y = \cos(x) + 1$

Q5 a)

The graph $y = \sin(2x)$ is enlarged along the x-axis by a scale factor ½.

b)

The graph $y = 2\sin(2x)$ is enlarged along the x-axis by a scale factor ½ and along the y-axis by a scale factor 2.

Q6

Whole graph moved up one unit on y-axis.

Q7

This is a reflection of $y = \sin(x)$ in the x-axis.

Q8

The graphs cross at about (48,6.8).
If $y = 10\cos x$ then $10y = 100\cos x$, so where the graphs cross,
$100\cos x = x + 20$. This can be rewritten as $20 = 100\cos x - x$, so the x value where the graphs cross is a solution to this equation.

Q9

X	0	10	20	30	40	50	60	70	80	90
sin x	0	0.17	0.34	0.5	0.64	0.77	0.87	0.94	0.98	1
(sin x)²	0	0.03	0.12	0.25	0.41	0.59	0.75	0.88	0.97	1

Q10

Graphs cross at about (24,0.3), so $x = 24$ is an approximate solution to $x = 10\sin(x) + 20$.

Graphs: Shifts and Stretches
P.117-P.118

Q1 a) to d)

e) and f)

g) and h)

Q2 a) to d)

e) and f)

g) to i)

Q3 a) and b)

Q4 a) and b)

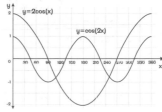

Answers: P.119 — P.124

Q5 **a)** to **d)**

e) to **g)**

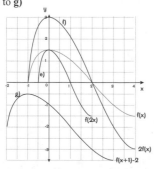

Loci and Constructions P.119-P.121

Q1

Not to scale

Q2

Not to scale

Length BA = 0.9 cm

Q3

Not to scale

Q4

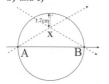

Radius of the circle = 2.7 cm

Q5 **a)** A circle with diameter AB.
b) and **c)**

Not to scale

d) The ship comes 1.7 cm = 0.85 km from the rocks.

Q6

Not to scale

Q7 **a)**

b) Distance around dashed path =
$(2 \times 100) + (\pi \times 65) = 404.2$ m

Q8

Not to scale

Q9 **a)**

b) Length = 8.6 cm equivalent to 43 km.
c) 35 km in 2.5 hrs, so speed
$= \frac{35}{2.5} = 14$ km/h.
d) and **e)** see diagram

Conversion Factors and Metric & Imperial Units P.122-P.124

Q1
a) 200 cm   **m)** 72 in
b) 33 mm   **n)** 80 oz
c) 4000 g   **o)** 100 yd 1 ft
d) 0.6 kg   **p)** 6000 mm
e) 48 in   **q)** 2000 kg
f) 3 ft   **r)** 3 kg
g) 7 ft 3 in   **s)** 86 mm
h) 2 lb 11 oz   **t)** 42 in
i) 0.65 km   **u)** 71 oz
j) 9000 g   **v)** 0.55 tonnes
k) 0.007 kg   **w)** 354 cm
l) 0.95 kg   **x)** 7 mm

Q2 147 kg $\times 2\frac{1}{4}$ = 330.8 lbs (1 d.p.)

Q3 14 gallons = 14 $\times$ 4.5 = 63 litres

Q4 9 stone 4 lbs = 9 + $\frac{4}{14}$ = 9.286 st.
$= 9.286 \div 0.157 = 59.1$ kg

Q5 Barry cycled 30 miles = 30 $\times$ 1.6 = 48 km.
So Barbara cycled furthest.

Q6 **a)** 11 in = 11 $\times$ 2.5 = 27.5 cm
b) 275 mm

Q7 **a)** 750 cm = 750 $\div$ 2.5 = 300 in
b) 750 cm = 7.5 m
c) 750 cm = 7500 mm
d) 750 cm = 0.0075 km

Q8 5 lb = 5 $\div$ $2\frac{1}{4}$ = 2.2 kg. So Dick needs to
buy <u>3 bags</u> of sugar.

Q9 **a)** £148.65   **g)** £81.50
b) £62.19   **h)** £13.51
c) £679.18   **i)** £272.65
d) £100   **j)** £307.25
e) £1.36   **k)** £408.16
f) £795.92   **l)** £0.68

Q10 **a)** 60 kg = 60 $\times$ $2\frac{1}{4}$ = 135 lbs
b) 135 lbs = 135 $\times$ 16 = 2160 oz.
c) 0.059 t = 59 kg, so Arnold can lift most.

Q11 **a)** 20 000 cm = 200 m
b) 200 000 cm = 2000 m = 2 km
c) 700 000 cm = 7000 m = 7 km
d) 200 000 000 cm^2 = 20 000 m^2
$= 0.02$ km^2

Q12 **a)** 1.67 m
b) 33.3 cm
c) 0.33 cm $\times$ 0.33 cm = 0.11 cm^2
d) 0.056 cm^2

Q13 **a)** £4.69
b) £51.07

Q14 Beer in the hotel costs 4 $\times$ 0.568 = €2.27
per pint.
€2.27 $\div$ 1.15 = £1.98
So the beer is better value in the hotel.

Q15 1 m = 1.1 yards, so 1 m^2 = (1.1 yd)^2
$= 1.21$ yd^2.
£10.80 per sq. m = £10.80 $\div$ 1.21
$= £8.93$ per sq. yard.
So the fabric superstore is cheaper.

Q16 **a)** 5.00 am   **b)** 2.48 pm
c) 3.16 am   **d)** 3.58 pm
e) 10.30 pm   **f)** 12.01 am

Q17 **a)** 2330   **b)** 1022
c) 0015   **d)** 1215
e) 0830   **f)** 1645

Q18 145 minutes

Q19 **a)** 8 hours
b) 10 hours
c) 11 hours 56 minutes
d) 47 hours 48 minutes

Q20 **a)** 3 hours 15 minutes
b) 24 minutes
c) 7 hours 18 minutes
d) 1 hour 12 minutes

Q21 **a)** $2\frac{1}{3}$ hours
b) 3.1 hours
c) $\frac{1}{3}$ of an hour

Answers: P.125 — P.130

Formula Triangles P.125

Q1

a) $A = 4.5 \times 6 = 27$ cm²
b) $h = 26/2 = 13$ cm
c) $b/2 = 49/3.5 = 14$
   so $b = 28$ cm

Q2

a) $g = 2/10 = 1/5$
b) $h = 18 \times 1/6 = 3$ m
c) $l = 3 \div 2/3 = 4.5$ m

Q3

a) $c = \pi \times 72 = 226$ cm (to nearest cm)
b) $d = 21/\pi = 6.7$ cm (to 1 d.p.)
c) $d = 2r - 250/\pi - 79.6$
   $r = 39.8$ cm (to 1 d.p.)

Q4

a) $L = 120/8 = 15$
b) $Q = 408/24 = 17$
c) $S = 0$

Speed, Distance and Time P.126-P.127

Q1 60 km/h

Q2 165 miles

Q3 2 hours 40 minutes

Q4

Distance Travelled	Time taken	Average Speed
210 km	3 hrs	70 km/h
195 miles	4 hrs 30 mins	30 mph
105 km	2 hrs 30 mins	42 km/h
9 miles	45 mins	12 mph
640 km	48 mins	800 km/h
70 miles	1 hr 10 mins	60 mph

Q5 a) $100/11 = 9.09$ m/s (to 2d.p)
   b) 32.73 km/h

Q6 7 minutes to go 63 miles so 540 mph.

Q7 $\frac{260}{71}$ hours = 3.66 hrs ≈ 3 hrs 40 min

   07.05 to 10.30 is 3 hrs 25 mins.
   Journey takes over 3 hrs 25 mins so No.

Q8 a) 98.9 mph (to 3 s.f.)
   b) 72.56 seconds
   c) 99.2 mph (to 3 s.f.)

Q9 a) $2.77 + 1.96 + 0.6 = 5.33$ hrs
      (to 3 s.f.) = 5 hours 20 mins
   b) 250 miles
   c) 46.9 mph (to 3 s.f.)

Q10 2.15 pm

Q11 a) 2.23 hrs (2 hrs 14 mins)
   b) 1 hr 49 mins + 10 mins
      = 1 hr 59 mins
   c) 1346 and 1401

Q12 The first athlete ran at $16000 \div (60 \times 60)$
   = 4.44 m/s, so was faster than the second
   athlete (at 4 m/s). The first athlete would
   take 37.5 mins to run 10 km; the second
   would take 41.7 mins.

Q13 a) 487.5 km
   b) 920.8 km
   c) 497 km/h

Q14 a) 8.13 m/s
   b) 7.30 m/s

Q15 a) 220 km
   b) 5 mins

Q16 180 m at 42 mph takes 4 hrs 17 mins. 180
   m at 64 mph takes 2 hrs 49 mins. So it
   stops for 1 hr 28 mins.

Q17 a) 4.8 m/s   b) 14.4 m/s
   c) 14.4 m/s   d) 17.3 km/h, 51.8 km/h,
                     51.8 km/h.

Q18 2.05 mins, 2.07 mins, 2.13 mins.

Density P.128

Q1 a) 0.75 g/cm³   b) 0.6 g/cm³
   c) 0.8 g/cm³   d) 700 kg/m³
                     = 0.7 g/cm³

Q2 a) 62.4 g   b) 96 g
   c) 3744 g (3.744 kg)
   d) 75 g

Q3 a) 625 cm³
   b) 89.3 cm³ (to 3 s.f.)
   c) 27778 cm³ (27800 to 3 s.f.)
   d) 2500 cm³

Q4 34.71 g

Q5 20968 cm³

Q6 Vol. = 5000 cm³ = 5 litres

Q7 1.05 g/cm³

Q8 a) SR flour 1.16 g/cm³;
      granary flour 1.19 g/cm³
   b) 378 ml

Estimating P.129-P.130

Q1 a) $6500 \times 2 = 13\,000$
   b) $8000 \times 1.5 = 12\,000$
   c) $40 \times 1.5 \times 5 = 300$
   d) $45 \div 9 = 5$
   e) $35\,000 \div 7000 = 5$
   f) $\frac{55 \times 20}{10} = 55 \times 2 = 110$
   g) $7000 \times 2 = 14\,000$
   h) $100 \times 2.5 \times 2 = 500$
   i) $20 \times 20 \times 20 = 8000$
   j) $8000 \div 80 = 100$
   k) $62\,000 \div 1000 = 62$
   l) $3 \div 3 = 1$

Q2 Approximately $15\,000 - (1500 + 2500 +$
   $1500 + 1500 + 3000) = 5000$

Q3

   Area under the graph ≈ area of triangle = $\frac{1}{2}$
   $\times 30 \times 10 = 150$

Q4 a) $4 \times 7 = 28$ days
   b) $14\,634 \div 28 = 522.6$ tins
   c) $15\,000 \div 30 = 1500 \div 3 = 500$ tins

Q5 a) $3 = 3.0000000$, $\frac{22}{7} = 3.1428571$,

      $\sqrt{10} = 3.1622777$, $\frac{255}{81} = 3.1481481$,

      $3\frac{17}{120} = 3.1416667$

   b) $3\frac{17}{120}$ is the most accurate of these

      estimates.

Q6 a) $\frac{150 + 50}{150 - 50} = \frac{200}{100} = 2$

   b) $\frac{20 \times 10}{\sqrt{400}} = \frac{200}{20} = 10$

   c) $\frac{2000 \times 4}{20 \times 5} = \frac{8000}{100} = 80$

   d) $\frac{10^2 \div 10}{4 \times 5} = \frac{10}{20} = 0.5$

Q7 a) 25 cm × 40 cm = 1000 cm².
   b) 5 km × 4 km = 20 km².

Q8 a) 39 m²   b) 3 tins

Q9 a) $3 \times 2^2 \times 9 = 108$ cm³
   b) $3 \times 5^2 \times 22 = 1650$ cm³

Q10 Mark's tank is approximately
   4500 cm³, so it won't be big enough.

Vectors P.131

Q1 a)

   b) i) $\binom{-1}{-4}$
      ii) $\binom{4}{0}$
      iii) $\binom{5}{4}$
   c) Isosceles

Q2 a) $\binom{2}{1}$

   b) $\binom{2}{5}$

c) $\binom{6}{-2}$ 2r

d) $\binom{1}{1}$ s+p

e) $\binom{6}{10}$ 2p-2s

f) $\binom{-1}{-8}$ 3q+s

g) $\binom{6}{0}$ 2r-q

h) $\binom{6}{-3}$ ½q+2r

i) $\binom{0}{-1}$ p+2s

j) $\binom{-6}{0}$ q-2r

Q3
a) $2y$ **d)** $2y + 2x$
b) $y + x$ **e)** $4y + 2x$
c) $-y - x$ **f)** $2x$

Q4
a)
i) $\overrightarrow{ED}$ or $\overrightarrow{AF}$ **v)** $\overrightarrow{BE}$
ii) $\overrightarrow{EF}$ or $\overrightarrow{DC}$ **vi)** $\overrightarrow{AC}$
iii) $\overrightarrow{AE}$ **vii)** $\overrightarrow{EC}$ or $\overrightarrow{AB}$
iv) $\overrightarrow{BA}$ **viii)** $\overrightarrow{EB}$
b) i) 48 cm²   **ii)** 60 cm²

Real-Life Vectors P.132

Q1 9.5 km/h

Q2 **a)** 55°
     b) 2.9 km/h

Q3 **a)** 353°
     b) 595 km/h

Q4
i) a) 15.6 N
     b) 40°
ii) a) 18.0 N
     b) 34°
iii) a) 30.5 N
     b) 41.0°